INTRODUCTION

This book is aimed at those who wish to learn more about red meat, the Scottish red meat industry and methods of production. Each chapter is packed with information to help you fully appreciate and make the most of Scotch Beef, Scotch Lamb and Specially Selected Pork.

Scotland's red meat industry enjoys a well-deserved reputation for producing excellent tasting Scotch Beef, Scotch Lamb and Specially Selected Pork. With generations of tradition and expertise, Scottish farmers rear livestock in a pristine environment with a particular focus on areas of animal health and welfare. These attributes are just some of the reasons that make our brands the customer's choice.

Additionally, the Scottish red meat industry is supported by a fully integrated Quality Assurance programme which ensures modern production methods with complete traceability throughout the entire chain of production and processing.

In recognition of the quality and regional attributes of Scotch Beef and Scotch Lamb, the EU awarded the products PGI (Protected Geographical Indication) status to help shoppers identify the genuine products produced in accordance with the Quality Meat Scotland Schemes.

This book is available to download from www.qmscotland.co.uk

Produced in collaboration with The Scotch Beef Club & The Scotch Butchers Club.

PLATE *5*

KITCHEN *38*

BUTCHER *68*

ABATTOIR *86*

FARM *108*

No. 1

PLATE

Many of today's customers are well informed about meat and want to know where and how it was produced. The strict assurances which underpin Scotch Beef, Scotch Lamb and Specially Selected Pork provide the guarantees required for even the most discerning of customers.

CONSUMER REQUIREMENT

The decisions shoppers and diners make about when, what and where to eat drive the industry and never before has there been so much choice. In recent years however, customers are generally more aware of food production with many shoppers more knowledgeable on the practices involved in rearing animals for meat.

Today's customer

Customer behaviour has changed in recent years as a result of many economic and environmental factors including the recent recession, food inflation and greenhouse gases.

Shoppers are paying greater attention to the price of the groceries they purchase and have taken advantage of the increasing number of promotions when buying products. However, different regions and demographics have different sets of priorities. Indeed, there are notable differences between Scottish shoppers and the rest of the UK in particular. When it comes to meat, Scots are generally willing to pay more for quality fresh red meat*.

Customers are also increasingly aware of the ethical values associated with the food products they consume. For instance the number of shoppers specifically buying Fairtrade products has increased threefold over the last four years from 9% in 2006 to 27% in 2010*.

A focus on animal health and welfare has been heightened in recent years as customers become better educated on the methods involved in meat production. Over one in four shoppers remain concerned about the living conditions of animals with approximately one in five shoppers specifically buying higher welfare products each month.

Health remains an important driver in many market sectors with consumers increasingly concerned about the use of additives in food products and salt levels in particular.

Concerns about the environment we live in also play a role in today's consumer behaviour. We may see this develop as a driver of product choice in the years ahead with an impact on industry in terms of labelling and an increased scrutiny on food packaging and waste. The growing use of re-usable shopping bags is an early manifestation of the "greener" shopper with 46% of shoppers in Britain now committed to bringing their own bags with them on their shopping journey.

Source: IGD – Shopper Trends (2010)

Customers are also increasingly aware of the ethical values associated with the food products they consume.

 QMS Assurance takes account of the latest customer insight to ensure the brands meet customer expectations. This takes place annually and involves stakeholders from trade as well as the Scottish SPCA, Scotland's animal welfare charity. For more information on the Assurance Schemes, visit page 112.

PLATE 7

Red meat is a major indicator of quality in foodservice

Red meat is one of the key products by which the increasingly discerning and knowledgeable consumer will judge the quality of their eating experience. Let's look at the facts:

- Over 720 million kg of red meat is served to British consumers eating out in pubs, restaurants and canteens every year.
- The amount of beef and lamb consumed out of the home is increasing.

- Across the total foodservice market, approximately 26% of all protein purchased, by weight, is beef and approximately 7% is lamb, with the proportions considerably higher in some sectors. *(Source: Quarterly Protein Monitor October 2004)*
- 42% of main courses on UK menus feature red meat, compared with 18% featuring poultry and 16% fish and seafood. *(Source: Menurama January 2007)*

Approximately 26% of all protein purchased, by weight, is beef and approximately 7% is lamb.

The Importance of Red Meat in Foodservice

RED MEAT MARKET SHARE – MAIN COURSES

SPECIES SHARE OF MAIN COURSE RED MEAT

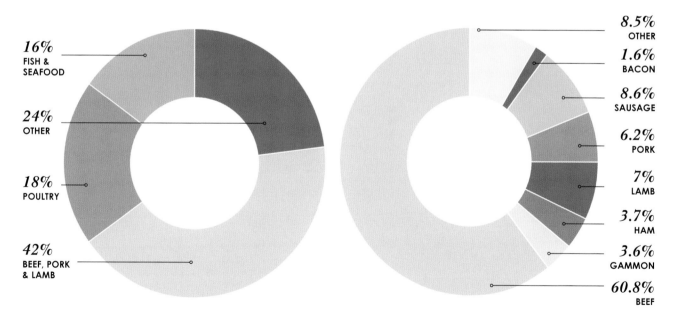

 It is very important that the caterer buys, prepares and serves red meat of the highest quality.

Consumer attitudes to red meat production

When thinking about the red meat industry, many consumers are happy to think only about animals on farms and about the meat they buy whether in a butcher, supermarket or restaurant. Most are uncomfortable and largely ignorant about the processes in between.

When prompted, however, we see interesting trends in behaviour over a period of time – and this information is used to influence the QMS Assurance standards. According to data published in 2010, the main concern for shoppers is the conditions in which animals are living. Over a period of several years, this particular area of concern has grown and is important to virtually half of all consumers. However, the research did highlight a range of other priorities for shoppers when considering meat production.

Consumer Top Five Priorities

1. Animal living conditions

2. Safety of the animal feed

3. Farm hygiene

4. Animals are slaughtered humanely

5. Meat has no additives

In the latest survey, fewer shoppers expressed concern about factory hygiene, farm hygiene or food scares compared with the same study one year ago*.

Most respondents in the research were generally very confident in Scotland's red meat production standards.

*Source: IGD – QMS Consumer Tracking Research (2010)

1. *Scotland's environment is hugely beneficial to the animals and to meat production.*

2. *Scotch Beef and Scotch Lamb are traditionally grass fed.*

3. *No artificial growth hormones are used.*

4. *Only highly skilled, licenced slaughter professionals are employed.*

5. *A fresh natural product is key, nothing is added to the meat.*

 For more information on Scottish specific assurance, see the Farm section, page 112.

PLATE 9

QMS has recently championed a collaboration with the Scottish SPCA, Scotland's animal welfare charity, to highlight the very high standards of pig welfare prevalent in Scotland.

Specially Selected Pork

Specially Selected Pork is the term given to pork products from the QMS Assurance Scheme. Unlike Scotch Beef and Scotch Lamb, Specially Selected Pork does not have PGI status and this is one of the reasons for the different brand terminology. However, Specially Selected Pork is reared and slaughtered under very similar assurances to the QMS cattle and sheep standards.

Furthermore, in response to heightened concern about pig welfare across Europe, QMS has recently championed a collaboration with the Scottish SPCA, Scotland's animal welfare charity, to highlight the very high standards of pig welfare prevalent in Scotland. All pig farms in the QMS scheme are visited by a Scottish SPCA Inspector to validate the welfare on farm. The 'Approved by the Scottish SPCA' brand mark can be used to promote these excellent credentials to retail or foodservice customers.

 More information about the Scottish SPCA can be found at www.scottishspca.org

Keep your customers informed and give them what they want

The retail sector is leading the way with meat labelling to show country of origin of meat products.

When shoppers are eating out of the home environment, either in a restaurant, pub or take-away, research shows that they are increasingly demanding more information.

- **71% of consumers believe that the meat they are eating in the out-of-home market is of UK origin.**

- **But in fact, UK-produced meat in the total foodservice market is only around 40%.**

- 61% of diners wanted to know where meat eaten outside the home came from: an increase from 55% just two years ago.

- 84% of respondents said they would like an easily recognised symbol on the menu.

- 80% reported they would be happy to see the country of origin included in the menu description.

Caterers therefore have an excellent opportunity to satisfy this consumer demand by proclaiming meat origins. Remember, as long as the animal is QMS Assured, all cuts (including economical options such as mince and diced products) are eligible to utilise the Scotch Beef, Scotch Lamb or Specially Selected Pork brand(s) on-pack or on the menu.

From top London restaurants to small, provincial pub kitchens, Scotch Beef delivers every time.

For more information on Country Of Origin Labelling (COOL) legislation in the foodservice and / or menu transparency, contact QMS or check on the website *www.scotchbeefclub.org.uk*

PLATE 11

MENU TRANSPARENCY: 8 SIMPLE GUIDELINES

1. Country of origin details should be provided for all dishes on the menu where the major prominent ingredient is meat-based. The term 'meat' in this context includes red meat, poultry and offal.

2. Information on the origin of meat should be made available either on the menu or clearly displayed on a poster, chalkboard or other point-of-sale material. Website information is not sufficient.

3. The term 'origin' in this context refers to where the animal has spent the majority of its life. Where appropriate, more than one country should be specified (for example when meats of different origins are used).

4. Caterers may wish to provide reference to the specific region, or even the farm that the animal has come from.

5. Caterers buying meat from more than one country should simply indicate their sourcing policy with a short explanation on the menu. For example: 'We source our meat from around the world or 'the meat served in this restaurant is Scotch except where otherwise stated.'

6. If it is the case that the origin of meat supplied will change before the menu is renewed, this should also be indicated. For example: 'the meat served in this restaurant is selected according to seasonal availability. Lamb is from Scotland or New Zealand, unless otherwise stated.'

7. If reference to the breed is included on the menu, this should still be supported with country of origin details. For example Aberdeen Angus originated in Scotland but is now also reared throughout the world.

8. Brand names implying origin of meat on the menu should also be clarified with origin details, for example: 'Highland Lambs from Scotland' or 'Scotch Premier Beef.'

Information on the origin of meat should be made available either on the menu or clearly displayed on a poster.

Examples of menu transparency:

Satisfaction is simple

Recognised brands: Scotch Beef, Scotch Lamb and Specially Selected Pork

+

Quality Meat Scotland's menu transparency

⎤ Consumer satisfaction

= Price premium & profit ⎤ Chef satisfaction

 How informative are your menus?

MEAT EATING TRADITIONS

Consumers and patrons doubtless vary in their meat tastes but for some, their choice is based on adherence to religious faiths or to principles which by choice, preclude them from eating products of animal origin.

Religious restrictions

Some religious faiths have particular requirements about the meat that they eat. In the UK this applies predominantly to members of the Muslim and Jewish religions amongst others:

- **Muslim**: 'Halal' means 'lawful' and this is the method used by Muslims. In the context of red meat it applies to lamb (and mutton) and to beef, but never pork. A slaughterman kills the animal by a single cut across the throat whilst saying "Bismilla Allah Akbar." Slaughter is generally very fast and efficient, see page 95 for more information. 'Haram' – 'unlawful' – is the opposite of Halal. Pork and unlawfully slaughtered beef and lamb are Haram.

- **Judaism**: The Jewish slaughter method is called Shechita, and the meat produced is Kosher meat.

- **Sikhism**: Sikhs do not see beef as taboo. A non-vegetarian Sikh can take beef, lamb or pork as readily as any other meat.

- **Hinduism**: States that Hindus have to be careful about food because what they eat decides physical and mental wellbeing. Eating animal meat or heavy food may lead to the strengthening of animal qualities and lethargic nature in us. One belief suggests that killing innocent and helpless animals for the purpose of satiating hunger is bad karma with harmful consequences. However, not all Hindus avoid eating meat and Hindu law books do not prohibit the eating of meat in general, but only certain types of meat.

Customer preferences

Vegetarians and vegans

The principle categories of vegetarians are:

- **vegetarians** – who do not eat fish, meat or poultry. Some however are selective and will eat fish or poultry or some specific meats like bacon but still call themselves vegetarians.

- **vegans** – who will not eat any food of animal origin, including, for example, milk or eggs.

- **ovolactarians** – who adhere to the same restrictions as vegans, but do include milk and eggs in their diet.

- **lactarians** – who adhere to the same restrictions as vegans, but do include milk in their diet (but not eggs).

- **herbivores** – who will eat only plants.

- **fruitarians** – who will eat only fruits.

- **granivores** – who will eat only seeds and grain.

Meat allergy

A very small number of people have an allergic reaction to a particular meat. Processed meats sometimes contain other ingredients, particularly milk, so it is possible for someone who is allergic to milk to react to a meat product. Beef and pork allergies are extremely rare and there is no known allergy to lamb.

Organic and free range meat

The caterer should be clear about these terms:

- Organic meat should be produced by breeding and rearing animals with regard to their welfare and by 'traditional and natural' methods. The term is tightly controlled by legislation.

- 'Free-range' is a rather vague term which describes a wide range of systems of keeping animals in 'unconfined' groups. By definition, most Scotch Beef and Scotch Lamb, which has been allowed to roam and feed freely on the hillside pastures for much of the year, is free range.

British Society for Allergy and Clinical Immunology: www.bsaci.org
Allergy UK: www.allergyuk.org SOPA: www.sopa.org.uk The Soil Association: www.soilassociation.org
SEERAD: www.scotland.gov.uk/topics/agriculture

PLATE 13

NUTRITION –
GETTING THE BALANCE RIGHT

There is much confusion today about the role of beef, lamb and pork products in a healthy diet. Indeed, a small number of consumers avoid meat products because they fear it is bad for their health.

The truth of the matter is that red meats have a high nutrition density. In other words, they contain a wide variety of nutrients in useful amounts which are easily absorbed by the body. Meat is an important source of B vitamins, including B-12, which is not found naturally in foods of plant origin. Meat also contributes trace elements and minerals to the diet, particularly iron and zinc.

No single food contains all the nutrients needed for good health, so the aim should be to include a wide variety of foods in the diet: balance is the key.

Meat and fat

Fatty red meat and meat products are often cited as major contributors to excessive fat (particularly saturated fat) in the diet. However, over-simplistic advice that fat reduction can be achieved by simply eating less red meat is unnecessary and incorrect. The National Food Survey has estimated that red meat products contribute only 22% of the total fat in the average diet and with new initiatives in place, the fat content of red meat on average has decreased significantly over recent years. Lean red meat is actually quite low in fat at 4–8g per 100g.

Healthier ways of cooking

- Choose lean cubes of beef, lamb or pork for casseroles or kebabs.
- Trim fat from meat before cooking.
- Cut off any remaining fat on the meat before serving.

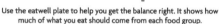

Use the eatwell plate to help you get the balance right. It shows how much of what you eat should come from each food group.

Department of Health in association with the Welsh Assembly Government, the Scottish Government and the Food Standards Agency in Northern Ireland.

© Crown copyright 2011

- Try these healthier cooking methods:
  - Dry frying, grilling, roasting on a rack or stir-frying.
  - Drain and discard fat from the pan before making gravy/sauce.
  - Skim fat from casseroles and stews before serving.
  - Dab or shake any grilled or fried food before serving.

Red meat makes an important contribution to a healthy, balanced diet.

For more information log onto www.nutrition.org.uk or www.food.gov.uk/scotland or www.bda.uk.com or www.eatwell.gov.uk

Meat and iron

The mineral iron is vital for red blood cell formation and is therefore essential at all stages of life. Too little iron in the diet can lead to the development of iron deficiency anaemia, which can make people tired, irritable and less able to concentrate.

Meat and health

A number of studies show an association between the types and amounts of food we eat and certain diseases such as heart disease and cancer. Some of the studies have suggested a potential link between eating excessive levels of red and processed meat and the chance of developing cancer. In the majority of these studies the levels of meat eaten is much higher than the 80-90 gm per person per day recommended in the UK, and none of the studies have shown meat to be the cause of cancer.

A number of the studies also show the importance of eating a balanced diet and eating different types of meat cooked by different methods. So eating a balanced diet with at least 5 portions of fresh fruit and vegetables per day can reduce the risk; especially eating cruciferous vegetables like broccoli (eg. Juge et al 2007).

A number of studies show an association between the types and amounts of food we eat and certain diseases, such as heart disease and cancer.

What are the levels of fats, vitamins and minerals in lean meat and how does red meat compare with chicken?

Lean red meat has a lower level of cholesterol than roast meat & chicken skin but a higher level of Vitamin B12, Iron and Zinc.

Product	Total fat in 100g	Saturated fat in 100g	Unsaturated fat in 100g	Cholesterol in 100g	Vitamin B12 in 100g	Iron in 100g	Zinc in 100g
Beef: Rump steak lean meat grilled	5.9g	2.5g	3.0g	76mg	3μg	3.6mg	5.6mg
Lamb: Whole leg lean meat medium roasted	9.4g	3.8g	4.5g	100mg	2μg	1.8mg	4.6mg
Pork: Leg joint lean meat medium roasted	5.5g	1.9g	3.0g	100mg	1μg	1.1mg	3.2mg
Chicken: Leg quarter roast meat and skin	16.9g	4.6g	11.0g	115mg	1μg	0.8mg	1.7mg

Source: McCance and Widdowson's The Composition of Foods, 6th summary edition 2002, Food Standards Agency.

  For information on 'marbling', see the Butcher section, page 80.

PLATE 15

How much iron?

On average, adult men need 8.7mg of iron a day, and women need 14.8mg. Here are some examples of how much iron various foods deliver:

FOOD	SERVING SIZE	IRON SUPPLIED PER 100g
Thick slices of lean roast beef	90g	2.3mg
A boiled egg	50g	1.0mg
Wholemeal bread (1 average slice)	36g	1.0mg
Dark roast turkey meat (average serving)	120g	1.7mg
A portion of lamb's liver, fried	100g	10.0mg
Canned sardines in oil	50g	1.5mg
Spring greens, boiled	90g	1.3mg
An average bowl of fortified breakfast cereal	45g	3.0mg
Beef, average, trimmed lean, raw	–	1.8mg
Lamb, average, trimmed lean, raw	–	1.4mg

Source: supplement to McCance and Widdowson's The Composition of Foods (Meat, Poultry and Game)
Source: Food Standards Agency Scotland, Meat and Livestock Commission

High levels of saturated fat in the diet can increase the amount of cholesterol in the blood and so increase the risk of heart disease.

The facts about fat

Some fat is needed in the diet because it helps the body absorb certain vitamins, it is a source of essential fatty acids, which the body can't make for itself, and it supplies energy. It is important not to have too much fat in the diet, so you should choose lower fat foods.

Fat is made up of saturated and unsaturated fatty acids. Saturated fatty acids are usually solid at room temperature and generally come from animal sources. High levels of saturated fat in the diet can increase the amount of cholesterol in the blood and so increase the risk of heart disease. Different food groups contribute different amounts of total and saturated fat in the diet, so it is important to choose a balanced diet, which is not too high in saturated fat.

Unsaturated fatty acids can be good for your health. They can be divided into two groups, monounsaturated fatty acids or MUFAs, and polyunsaturated fatty acids or PUFAs. There are two families of PUFAs, the Omega 3 family and the Omega 6 family. Certain types of Omega 3 PUFAs have been shown to be good for heart health. These Omega 3 PUFAs are found in high levels in meat produced from animals grazed on grass. Health professionals inform us that our diet is lacking in Omega 3, so eating meat from grass fed beef or lamb could contribute to a healthy level of Omega 3 in your diet.

Food with more than 20g fat per 100g is considered to be **HIGH** in fat.
Food with less than 3g fat per 100g is considered to be **LOW** in fat.

IDENTIFICATION –
LABELLING FOR THE CONSUMER

It's important that shoppers receive the correct information on their products to make an informed decision on what products they buy. For example, if you choose to buy a pot of Cornish clotted cream, it's only right to expect it to come from Cornwall and, by buying that product, your choice will in some way benefit the producers of that particular product line.

So, if the product wasn't actually made there, the label must say so that, as a buyer, you're not treated unfairly or disadvantaged. There are a few well-known foods allowed to keep their names in spite of this rule. We know that Swiss rolls don't have to come from anywhere near the Alps and that Yorkshire pudding doesn't necessarily begin its life in the Dales.

Hopefully we've established that the more you know, the better you can make a decision on what product you wish to buy. Equally the less you know, the risk is greater that you will be misled.

To this end, it is illegal for labels and menus to provide false information or give misleading descriptions. Recent media attention has highlighted the opportunities available for some food manufacturers to stretch the truth when it comes to the origin of raw materials used in some products and/or dishes.

Meat (and beef in particular) is driving this heightened awareness and regulations are in place to help shoppers determine where their item originated and to what standards it was reared and processed.

Beef

Any pre-packed beef that you purchase must clearly state on its label the animal's country of birth, country or countries where it was reared, and the country of slaughter as well as the appropriate four digit slaughter and cutting plant (if different to slaughter plant) licence numbers.

Labelling rules for purchasing loose beef (bought over a counter in a butcher's shop for example) and in restaurants, are different to those that apply to pre-packed products. A Voluntary Scheme comes into play which means that the proprietor must be able to prove any claim they make about their beef.

The oval EU health mark on the label or wrapping has a reference number of the last place of processing or packaging, not of origin of the meat.

If the animal was reared and slaughtered in the same country as it was born, the label may simply state 'country of origin'. To be classed as Scotch Beef, the animal must have been born, reared for its whole life on a QMS Assured Farm and slaughtered in Scotland.

As a check, for example, all Scottish slaughter plant codes on-pack begin with the number '1' so although the product may say 'Slaughter in UK',

For professional and retail classification check page 94.

PLATE 17

the code will help you identify if it was slaughtered in Scotland.

The Trading Standards Agency within your Local Authority is responsible for checking that this compulsory information is always included on beef packaging. *www.tradingstandards.gov.uk/advice/approved-traders.cfm*

Are there any exceptions?

These labelling standards apply only to fresh and frozen beef. Beef products with added ingredients – such as Beef Wellington or peppered steak – do not fall under the same EU regulations highlighted above. As another example, beef mince must only display a batch number, purely for identification purposes, and does not carry the oval EC health mark.

Scotch Beef and Scotch Lamb brands have, for many years, held a Protected Geographical Indication (PGI). When an agricultural product or other foodstuff is given a PGI, you know that its name is protected and that it comes from a specific region or country, and that this origin grants the item a certain quality, reputation or other characteristic as a result.

Currently pork, lamb and venison products do not share the same levels of labelling legislation which are apparent in beef but legislation will be harmonised to cover all meats. However, many suppliers to retail and/or foodservice markets still utilise similar practices to help buyers decide what products to buy.

To be classed as Scotch Beef, the animal must have been born and reared for its whole life on a QMS assured farm and slaughtered in Scotland.

Lamb

The Scotch Lamb logo is used only for meat products from lambs born, raised for their whole life and slaughtered in Scotland as part of the QMS Assurance Scheme. Rigorous standards must be adhered to for the 'whole life' of the product – and independent annual inspections guarantee that businesses involved in producing, processing and preparing Scotch Lamb comply with these. As lamb is a seasonal product, Scotch Lamb is most plentiful from mid-August to the end of March.

Spring lamb doesn't mean lamb is available in spring but born in spring. In 2010, 48% of fresh lamb retailed in GB was imported. *(Source: Kontor)*

Pork

The Specially Selected Pork logo represents pork products from the QMS Assurance Scheme. It does not have PGI status but does still represent products which are reared to the strict assurance standards laid out in the QMS Schemes.

The FSA Scotland has produced a guide to food labelling available free of charge to consumers and professionals. See below for details.

In 2010, 27% of fresh pork sold in GB was imported. *(Source: Kontor)*

Terms & Symbols

The term 'Scottish' beside meat products, for example 'Scottish Beef' means only that the animal was born, raised and slaughtered in Scotland. The term does not reflect the same strict standards to which Scotch Beef is raised nor does it guarantee animal welfare. Scottish Beef may also include poorer quality meat which is not permitted in the Scotch Beef scheme.

Similarly, the use of a country's flag on a product, such as the Saltire or Union Jack, symbolises the origin of the product, but has no specific legally binding definition. Flags have no official meaning and should be viewed with caution especially when associated with processed meats. It is generally understood that some aspects of the process may have happened in the country. In any case, the symbol should not be misleading to the consumer.

Another area of confusion for some consumers is the use of breed terminology such as 'Aberdeen Angus Beef', 'Blackface Lamb' or 'Gloucester Old Spot Pork'. These terms must be viewed with caution as they refer only to the breed of animal – and are therefore not an indication of origin unless followed up by a suitable reference to the country of origin.

The use of a country's flag on a product, such as the Saltire or Union Jack, symbolises the origin of the product, but has no specific legally binding definition.

The FSA Scotland has produced a guide to food labelling, for more information visit:
www.food.gov.uk/aboutus/publications/scotpublications/

PLATE 19

LABELLING FOR THE PROFESSIONALS

To help safeguard the work of those in the 'Scotch' supply chain, and to satisfy their customers, many top restaurants highlight 'Scotch' on the menu as a distinct selling point. By investing in Scotland's fantastic meat industry, they're proud to shout about the origin, and assurances, of the products they sell.

A recent survey showed more than two thirds of caterers are not identifying meat origin on their menus. When asked about the origin of meat on menus, a staggering 71% believed the meat they were eating was home-produced. In fact, the actual figure is much closer to 40%!

Labelling is therefore becoming increasingly important as it can provide:

- Assurance on the integrity of your supply.
- A guarantee on production methods and assurances.
- Full product traceability from farm to plate.
- A competitive advantage for caterers and restaurants.

Protecting every link of the supply chain

The following operators must comply with the processes in place for fresh and frozen beef (not mince):

- Slaughterhouse • Cutting plant • Cold store
- Re-packaging centre • Re-wrapping centre
- Catering butchers

For beef from animals born, raised and slaughtered in the United Kingdom there are a minimum of four compulsory 'fields' of information:

- Reference code – this code links the meat on sale.
- Origin – UK (or British) – UK includes Scotland, England, Wales and Northern Ireland.
- Place of slaughter – 'UK', plus Licence number of slaughterhouse.
- Place of 'cutting' – 'UK', plus Licence number(s) of cutting plant(s).

The current list of Quality Meat Scotland approved abattoirs who can supply Scotch Beef or Scotch Lamb are:

Code	Plant name
1101	ABP (Perth)
1103	Woodhead Bros. Meat Company
1106	McIntosh Donald
1108	Mathers (Inverurie) Ltd
1110	Donald Russell Ltd.
1118	Stornoway Abattoir
1121	Scotch Premier Meat Ltd.
1125	John M. Munro Ltd.
1136	A P Jess
1137	Shetland Livestock Marketing Group
1144	St Andrews Abattoir
1156	Orkney Meat Ltd.
1160	Millers of Speyside
1508	Michael Malone of Edinburgh
1512	Grampian Country Pork Halls
1516	James Chapman (Butchers) Ltd.
1517	Wishaw Abattoir Ltd.
1533	John Scott Meat (Paisley)
1535	Sandyford Abattoir
1541	A K Stoddart Ltd.
1560	Scotbeef Ltd.
1594	Sandyford Foods
1598	Highland Meats (A Division of Dawn Meats UK Ltd.)
1633	P R Duff
1661	Barclay & Newton
1709	Lynch Quality Meats (Ayrshire) Ltd.

This list is correct at time of printing

A recent survey showed more than two thirds of caterers are not identifying meat origin on their menus.

For more information regarding beef labelling legislation at the retail level check: www.scotland.gov.uk and type 'beef labelling' into the search box or contact the Scotch Beef Club. See page 118.

How to read a slaughter tag on a carcase

For complete confidence, and to get a full guarantee of the provenance of the Scotch Beef being purchased, Chefs are encouraged to ask for a copy of the slaughter tag from their suppliers.

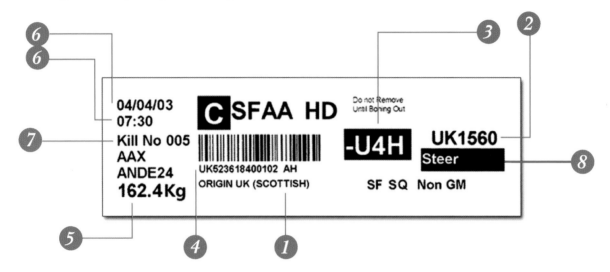

KEY

1. **Country of Origin**

This tells you where the beef came from e.g. the UK (or another country e.g. BR = Brazil, AR = Argentina). UK includes Scotland, England, Wales and Northern Ireland.

2. **Country of slaughter and licence number (EC Plant Code)**

Shows where the animal was slaughtered and licence number. Scotch Beef and Scotch Lamb always start with a '1' and must be a member of Quality Meat Scotland's Processor Assurance Scheme.

3. **Carcase classification**

This code reflects the animal's conformation and fatness (see page 94).

4. **Ear tag number**

Butchers will be able to identify the movement history of the animal from its records. To be classified Scotch Beef or Scotch Lamb, the animals must have only spent time on assured Scottish farms. On the passport, the holding number will start with a 66/ or greater, e.g. 84/568/0005. On the ear tag, the code must begin with UK5 in order to be Scotch.

5. **Side weight**

6. **Kill time and date**

7. **Kill number**

8. **Sex**

Notes

- If the country of origin ('birthplace'), rearing and slaughtering are the same (as it is with Scotch Beef), the labels may simply state 'country of origin' or 'Origin:UK.'

- Pre-wrapped meat must be labelled on its packaging. However, if packages are grouped together in a carton, the carton only needs to show the mandatories discussed above.

 For up to date information, visit www.qmscotland.co.uk and click on 'Members'.

PLATE 21

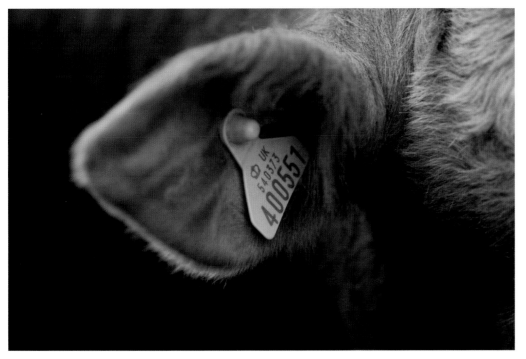

By law you are entitled to enquire as to the origin of the meat you are buying from your suppliers.

Further claims can be made but only with prior approval by the Beef Labelling Scheme (*www. scotland.gov.uk/Topics/farmingrural/Agriculture/ Livestock/Meat/Beef/Labelling/scheme*), including:

- Region – where the animal was born and reared.
- Breed or cross-breed (e.g. 'Galloway', 'Galloway cross' or 'Galloway sired').
- Age.
- Sex (male, female).
- Production method (e.g. organic, grass-fed).
- Slaughter method (e.g. Halal).
- Slaughter date.
- Maturation time.

Finally, criteria which can freely appear on labels include:

- Product name or cut e.g. rib eye, brisket.
- Product weight.
- 'Best before' and 'Use by' dates.
- Storage conditions e.g. 'Keep refrigerated'.
- Cooking instructions.
- Names and addresses of suppliers.
- Packaging statements.
- Reference to the carcase classification grid.
- The health mark required by the Fresh Meat Directive.
- PDO, PGI status (see page 22).

 For clarification of the definitions of 'Scotch' and 'Scottish' please see page 115. For more information on how to join the Scotch Butchers Club, see page 119.

ENSURING QUALITY

What is quality?

Quality is about delivering what your customers expect and more.

As Scotch Beef and Scotch Lamb are predominantly grass fed and reared naturally, e.g free of hormones, nature plays an important part in the quality of the meat. This includes the specific environment of the farm, the history of the animal, its age, sex and the type of grass that the animal chooses to eat.

Quality Meat Scotland Assurance Schemes – confidence for you and your customers

Quality Meat Scotland is committed to providing Assurance throughout the supply chain and embraces quality, safety, traditional husbandry and wholesomeness. Quality Meat Scotland research identified the following concerns that strongly influence consumer choice:

- "we are what we eat."
- "we need assurance that what we are feeding our animals will not harm us."
- "we want a transparent, clear system of assured quality we can trust."
- "we want standards policed in a way we can have confidence in."

Effective Assurance is a long-standing, integral part of the Scotch meat and livestock sector and Scotland was one of the first to recognise the market opportunity of offering assured products.

The Quality Meat Scotland Assurance Schemes guarantee that only animals from farms that meet the assurance standards are eligible to be classed and called Scotch Beef, Scotch Lamb or Specially Selected Pork. These farms are inspected by an independent organisation on an annual basis.

The classifications 'Scotch Beef' and 'Scotch Lamb' are given only to cattle or sheep that have been born and reared for their whole lives on an assured farm(s) in Scotland and then slaughtered at approved slaughterhouses in Scotland. We call this the 'whole-life' scheme as any animal which leaves Scotland, for even the smallest duration, loses the right to be branded as Scotch.

PGI and PDO status

The European Commission has developed the PGI (Protected Geographical Indication) and PDO (Protected Designation of Origin) systems. These qualifications protect foodstuffs across Europe and help consumers by giving them information about the specific character of products and a regional identity. Partly as a result of Scotland's excellent Assurance Schemes, but also due to satisfying the strict guidelines laid down, both Scotch Beef and Scotch Lamb have attained the important Protected Geographical Indication status from the European Union.

By law it is mandatory to show PGI or PDO logos next to the descriptor at point of sale.

Both Scotch Beef and Scotch Lamb have attained the important Protected Geographical Indication status from the European Union.

So why are the PGI and PDO so important? Here are some key reasons:

- The PGI definition matches consumer expectations and so protects our industry from consumer misconceptions and misleading product claims.
- Scotch Beef and Scotch Lamb generally carry a premium price in butchers, retail and restaurants which leaves it open for abuse to call meat and dishes 'Scotch' when they are not. PGI status makes this practice illegal.
- PGI and PDO have common status in Europe – e.g. Parma ham, feta cheese and Parmigiano Reggiano cheese – and so this qualification for our beef and lamb enhances the profile of our industry in other markets as a quality product.

The Protected Geographical Indications (PGI) for Scotch Beef and Scotch Lamb have been in force since 21st June 1996 but the definition of Scotch Beef has been subsequently tightened on 21st July 2004 and the definition of Scotch Lamb on 11th August 2004. Ever since, any time the terms Scotch Beef or Scotch Lamb are used, it means that the meat has met the PGI specifications. It is a legal requirement that the consumer is not misled in the event that Scotch and non-Scotch products are being sold in the same premises.

In contracts you may consider using the following wording in any communication to your supplier:

"The beef and lamb you supply to my business must meet the definition of Scotch as defined under the EU PGI legislation."

Definitions: Scotch: born in Scotland, reared all its life in Scotland, slaughtered in Scotland and always part of the Quality Assurance Scheme (welfare, feed, transport). **Scottish** or **product of Scotland** means the same but without the guarantees of Quality Assurance Scheme.

. . . .

Our PGI promise:
- *Quality guarantee*
- *Superior character*
- *Fully traceable and 100% Assured*
- *Clear labelling… Guaranteed Scotch*

. . . .

EC Council Regulation on the Protection of Geographical Indications and Designations of Origin Reg No 2081/92

Product must be produced and processed and prepared in geographical area (PDO)

Quality or characteristics essentially due to that area

**ORKNEY BEEF
ORKNEY LAMB
SHETLAND LAMB**

The geographical link must occur in at least one of the stages of production, processing or preparation. Furthermore, the product can benefit from a good reputation.

Specific quality, reputation or other characteristics attributable to that area

 For further information regarding PGI and PDO status please visit:
http://ec.europa.eu/agriculture/quality/schemes/index_en.htm

FLAVOUR QUALITY –
FLAVOUR CONSIDERATIONS

The flavour of meat develops during the cooking process through the effects of heat on the many compounds present and the reactions between them.

These include water-soluble compounds and fatty acids which are characteristic of the species' flavours. These elements may vary due to a number of factors, for example:

- Diet.
- 'Fatness.'
- Handling and processing.
- Ageing and packaging.
- Animal and breed.

These factors will be looked at in more detail in other parts of this section but the chart opposite delivers a snapshot of their impact.

WHAT CONSUMERS LOOK FOR IN THEIR MEAT EATING EXPERIENCE

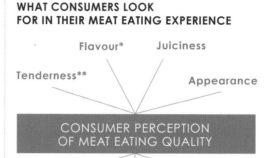

** *Very important*
* *Important*

The flavour of meat develops during the cooking process through the effects of heat on the many compounds present and the reactions between them.

Relative effects of production and processing factors on beef flavour

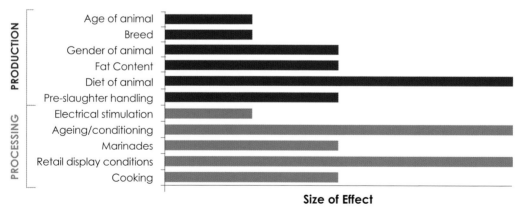

Source: Consumer Decision Tree, Meat and Livestock Commission 2004

 For more information on diet, see the Farm section, pages 106 – 111.

PLATE 25

What is Influencing Flavours

Based on data from a questionnaire used to identify key factors determining the purchase and consumer satisfaction of beef steaks, Robbins et al (2002) showed that colour, price, visible fat and cut were key drivers for purchase. However, tenderness, flavour and juiciness were most important in terms of eating satisfaction and this is most important for foodservice customers as they very rarely see the meat uncooked before being served.

Factors which can affect the flavour and therefore eating experience are age, breed, gender, fatness, diet and production systems (such as ageing).

Animal diet

Animal diet certainly has a significant – some would say the most significant – effect on flavour. It is generally agreed that animal diet is an important factor in fat type which in turn affects flavour. Animal diet can bring positive and negative traits to meat. For more information check page 111 in the Farm section.

Age

There are clear differences between veal and beef (Rodbotten et al (2004)). Beef has a higher overall flavour intensity and a lower acidity taste but with higher gamey, sweet and cloying qualities. There are also differences as a result of age in pigs (sow and pig) and sheep (lamb and mutton).

Breed

Significant speculation surrounds the role of breed in determining meat-eating quality and it is an area of research that is being looked at globally. It is generally felt that the differences in breed flavour are small and where they do exist, it is correlated to differences in fatness, with fatter animals tending to have higher intensity scores.

Gender

In the past, gender was a significant aspect of beef and lamb flavour. Gender remains a factor but modern production methods have reduced the variability. Bull beef from entire male cattle will give a more defined flavour.

. . . .

WET AGEING occurs when meat is aged in a vacuum packed environment.

DRY AGEING occurs when meat is exposed to the air.

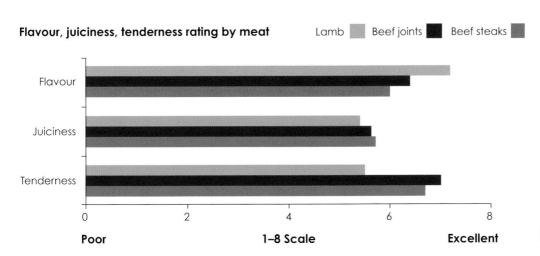

Flavour, juiciness, tenderness rating by meat   Lamb   Beef joints   Beef steaks

Source: Savell et al, 1979

. . . .

Seasonality

As seasons and weather affect animal feed and diet, it also influences the flavour of the meat. Pigs tend to have a consistent flavour as they are omnivores and don't depend on seasonal feed as much as beef and lamb. Scotch Lamb tend to have a more subtle flavour between August and February.

Marbling and fatness

Another area of much speculation is the phenomenon of marbling (see also Butcher section, page 80). Juiciness and flavour desirability scores tend to increase with an increase in marbling intensity. The difference of composition between muscles explains the difference of eating quality such as flavour and texture. In general, patties and burgers contain more fat than lean muscle, which has an effect on their tenderness, juiciness and beef flavours. In general grain-fed animals (see page 110) are more marbled than grass-fed. From experience, grass-fed is tastier, but grain-fed juicier due to the fat content.

Production system

Stressed cattle, be it at the farm, in transit or abattoir release stress hormones. If this is just pre-slaughter, Dark, Firm and Dry (DFD) meat can be produced due to an abnormal change in the muscle's pH. This has an affect on desirable flavours released in the cooking process and therefore delivers an ultimately inferior final product to the consumer. Occurrences of DFD however is very rare in the Scotch Assurance Scheme. Post-slaughter, some abattoirs use Electrical Stimulation (ES) which can offer some improvement in tenderness and eating quality. Carcases can be chilled rapidly after ES, rather than waiting for the internal muscle temperature to cool naturally.

Ageing on the bone / off the bone

Jeremiah and Gibson (2003) showed that vacuum packing or dry ageing of bone-in or boneless steaks for 4 weeks did not significantly affect the overall quality of the flavour. The data also suggests that bone-in vacuum packed cuts were perceived to have more intense beef flavour and 'fatty' aromatic flavours. Inappropriate 'livery' aftertastes were more intense in vacuum packed boneless products, while 'metallic' aromatic flavours were most intense in bone-in vacuum packed cuts.

It has been observed that bone-in, dry aged and bone-in vacuum packaged beef require shorter cooking times and result in lower cooking losses. However, both bone-in and boneless vacuum packed products had significantly higher overall palatability and flavour than dry aged beef. (Jeremiah and Gibson (2003).

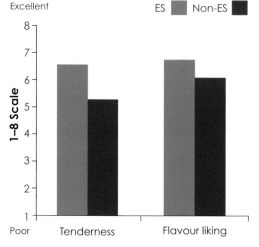

Lamb can be lean. This rack of lamb has been specified 'trimmed'.

Effects of Electrical Stimulation (ES) and Non- Electrical Stimulation (Non-ES) on tenderness and flavour of sirloin steaks

Source: Savell et al, 1979

  For more information on the terms used here, see Abattoir section page 88.

PLATE 27

Length of ageing (maturation)

After slaughter, ageing and packaging of meat also play an important part in the final eating qualities. This is dealt with further in the Kitchen section of this book from page 33. However the following tables summarise these effects:

- Ageing improves beef flavour (pooled results for all ageing treatments), particularly bone-in

vacuum packing. Dry ageing has been suggested as producing more tender, juicy flavoursome meat (Campbell et al 2001) with dry ageing for 20 days leading to the production of a sweet and milk-like aroma (Matsuishi et al (1993) referred to in Jeremiah and Gibson (2003)) and an intensification of the beef and browned flavour notes (Warren and Katsner (1992) referred to in Jeremiah and Gibson (2003))

Ageing improves beef flavour and dry ageing (although balanced by significant weight loss) is preferable to wet ageing. Ageing affects tenderness.

Effects of ageing on beef flavour

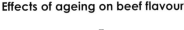

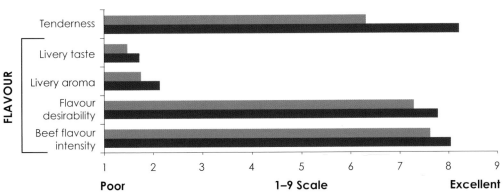

Source: Jeremiah and Gibson, 2003

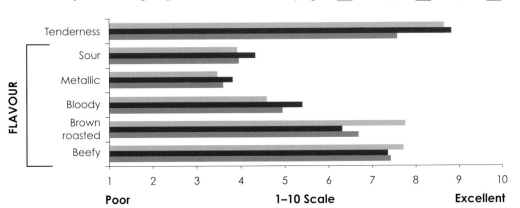

Source: Warren and Kastner, 1992

MATCHING BEEF, LAMB & PORK TO DRINKS

The world of wine has always been very subjective, where arguments based on personal preference are as valid as 'rules' adhered to across generations.

Talk to your wine supplier and your butcher to discuss great combinations for your menu.

If ever there was an occasion to bend rules, food matches with wine is it, but there are some guidelines which should certainly be considered before opening a bottle (even if they are subsequently ignored!).

The decision may be based on your mood, the climate where you are dining, accompaniments to the meats, the recommendations of your dining companions. Whatever the case, make sure you enjoy it!

The following guidelines offer wines that complement Scotch Beef, Scotch Lamb and Specially Selected Pork cuts, largely based on the flavours divulged by the meat characteristics in their own right and the method of cooking.

When barbecuing, beer or lager may be a good option to complement potential bitterness which may develop during the cooking process.

It's a matter of taste

Food and wine is such a personal choice. In fact it goes beyond wine. You may feel that a hop-rich bitter or a cold lager would go better with your meal. Perhaps a fortified wine to complement your dessert or how about a malt whisky to really marry that cranachan dessert…or it's Burn's Night!

Food is a celebration and anything that can augment that feeling – be it textbook combination or a fusion of flavours – should be your decision.

How to use these tables

Matching wine and food is often considered a bit of a mystery. It doesn't have to be. These are only examples of combinations that work. Simply use the chart as a guide and have fun experimenting and find out what works best for your taste.

PLATE 29

BEEF

DISH	COOKING METHOD	WINE STYLE	WINE /GRAPE VARIETY SUGGESTION
Steak	Pan fried	Rich, full bodied and refined. A little oak adds smoothness and depth	Cabernet Sauvignon, Chianti, Malbec or Rioja
Rib Steak	Grilled	Rich with a little more tannin to cut through the caramelisation caused by grilling	Cotes du Rhone - Syrah or Shiraz as it is know in the Southern hemisphere Pinotage or Barolo
Roast Beef	Oven Roasted	A smooth fleshy, rounded red with a bit of body	Pinot Noir, Cabernet Sauvignon, Malbec or a softer Merlot
Rump Steak	Grilled	Rounded and full-bodied. Deep flavoured, rich and even spicy	Cotes du Rhone, Shiraz. Pinotage, Grenache or Rioja
Braising Steak	Braised in oven	Softer, gentler reds. Match the wine to the braising liquid and the seasoning	Chinon, Cabernet Sauvignon, Valpolicella or Merlot. Remember, varietals from the New World tend to be fruitier and fuller.
Boeuf Bourguignon	Oven	Warm generous wines to complement the rich sauce	Pinot Noir, ideally from Burgundy or Italian Amarone or Montpulciano, rich red from Penedes in N E Spain
Pot-au-feu	Hob / oven	Medium bodied with depth of flavour and purity of fruit	Cabernet Sauvignon from Chile. Cru Beaujolais or soft Bordeaux from the Medoc
Oxtail	Hob / Oven	Rich, generous, even earthy reds	Burgundy, Chianti or simple rustic reds from Languedoc Roussillon

LAMB

DISH	COOKING METHOD	WINE STYLE	WINE /GRAPE VARIETY SUGGESTION
Roast New Season Lamb	Oven	Lighter, fresher reds with not too much tannin	New World Pinot Noir or Cru Beaujolais. Red from the Loire or Cabernet Sauvignon from Chile
Roast Rack of Lamb	Oven	More robust wine will work well with the rich roast flavours	Rioja, Pinotage or young full bodied wines from Southern France
Confit	Oven	Silky, plummy, full flavoured wines with a bit of tannin	Traditional grape varieties such as Merlot, Pinot Noir or Cabernet Sauvignon
Spicy, Asian style lamb dishes	All methods	Full flavoured, aromatic whites to complement the spices	Lychee flavoured Chilean Gewürztraminer is great with Thai food. Muscat or Semillon or wines from the Rhine
Navarin	Hob / oven	Big round flavoursome whites or lighter, fresher reds	Cotes du Rhone Blanc, New World Chardonnay, Vognier or whites from Tuscany and Umbria

PORK

DISH	COOKING METHOD	WINE STYLE	WINE /GRAPE VARIETY SUGGESTION
Roast leg or shoulder	Roast	Most people stick with red for pork. A full strong red will enhance the meat flavours and cut through any fat	Red – A fruity grenache (Rhone), rich pinot noir (Burgundy) or a cru Beaujolais go well. White – try the appley taste of white Semillon or Sauvignon Blanc from the Loire or even more fruity versions from New Zealand
Pork Chops	Grilled	Subtle reds not too weighty or acidic. Full flavoursome whites from the New World.	Chianti, Beaujolais or Sauvignon Blanc from California
Pork Sausages – bangers and mash	Oven / grill	Rich, spicy, berry flavoured reds are best	Cotes du Rhone, Australian Shiraz or full bodied Spanish Tempranillo
Gammon / ham – served cold	Baked or boiled	Flavoursome whites, rose or light reds which are low in tannin	Riesling or Vouvray. Light reds from Gamay grape or spiced berry roses from Spain or Bergerac
Roast / barbequed loin of pork	Oven or barbeque	Big full bodied whites or full flavoursome reds with good acidity	Well-aged Alsace Riesling. Cabernet Franc, Pinot Noir or Barbaresco

 For more information on the effects of alcohol, visit www.drinkaware.co.uk

SUPPLY CHAIN FOCUS
THE RECIPE FOR RESTAURANT SUCCESS

In the first of our supply-chain focus pages, we introduce the opportunities in fine dining with a look at the Scotch Beef Club and share some thoughts from a few leading chefs on Scotch Beef and Scotch Lamb. It is with their support and expertise that we maintain our reputation for delivering products of the highest quality.

The Scotch Beef Club is an impressive collection of restaurants, currently only within the UK, that are unashamedly based on quality. Its members are restaurants that are proud to serve Scotch Beef and proud to promote it on their menus. It is the natural final link in the Scottish chain of assurances that connects the Scottish farmer, the feed manufacturer, the Scottish auction market, the Scottish abattoir and the butcher to ensure that you, the consumer, know where your Scotch Beef or Scotch Lamb have come from and how they have been produced.

All the Michelin starred restaurants in Scotland are members, likewise some very prestigious places to eat in London and the Midlands of England. However, the Scotch Beef Club is not elitist; there are many members whose aspirations are more modest. They all have one thing in common; they care about their customers and want to offer them the best eating experience possible.

HRH Princess Royal is Honorary President of the Scotch Beef Club. Membership is restricted to no more than 300 per year and all new members are visited before membership is approved.

The Scotch Beef Club aims to organise Academy Courses and tasting events each year to help chefs understand more about

Her Royal Highness, The Princess Royal, patron of the Scotch Beef Club, welcoming one of the new ambassadors for Scotch Beef and Lamb, chef Christophe Marguin.

"At last, meat of exceptional quality with remarkable regularity, breeders who abide by very strict conditions, and abattoirs where people take the time to let the meat acquire a truly excellent condition. When I cook Scotch Beef I think of the marvellous landscapes in which I had the joy to work."

CHRISTOPHE MARGUIN
Chef, President of Lyon Toques Blanches and President of World Toques Blanches, Scotch Beef PGI & Scotch Lamb PGI Ambassador

PLATE 3

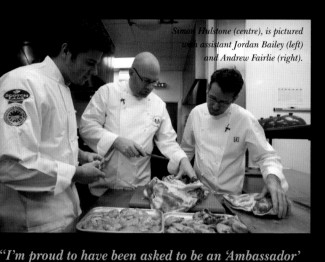

Simon Hulstone (centre), is pictured with assistant Jordan Bailey (left) and Andrew Fairlie (right).

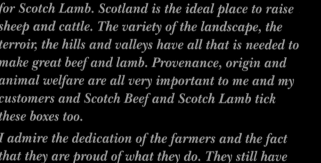

Cees Helder with David Ismail, Aberdeen Angus farmer.

"I'm proud to have been asked to be an 'Ambassador' for Scotch Lamb. Scotland is the ideal place to raise sheep and cattle. The variety of the landscape, the terroir, the hills and valleys have all that is needed to make great beef and lamb. Provenance, origin and animal welfare are all very important to me and my customers and Scotch Beef and Scotch Lamb tick these boxes too.

I admire the dedication of the farmers and the fact that they are proud of what they do. They still have patience to follow tradition, often with a modern twist, and focus on taking time to make the quality beef and lamb that I need."

SIMON HULSTONE

Chef Proprietor of The Elephant at Torquay (Michelin Star holder since 2006). UK representative in Bocuse d'Or 2009 and 2011. Knorr UK Chef of the Year 2010.

"Scotch Beef is for me the way to get the taste of beautiful Scotland at home. The robust taste sensation and the tenderness of the meat are unprecedented. Not only the sirloin or fillet but also other cuts of the beef are excellent. The major secret of the taste is the clean fresh Scottish air, optimal soil and carefully selected beef breeds. Maturation is possibly the most important "secret ingredient", it contributes to the excellent taste and texture of the beef. Beef is getting its full flavour.

As Ambassador for Scotch Beef and Scotch Lamb, I visit Scotland regularly. Only 30 minutes from the capital Edinburgh you can be in the middle of the Scottish hills in amongst the proud farmers and their cattle."

CEES HELDER

President Patron Cuisiniers The Netherlands, first Dutch three star Michelin Chef.

For more information on The Scotch Beef Club or to apply for membership, please refer to page 118 or visit:

www.scotchbeefclub.org

No. 2
KITCHEN

Scotch Beef, Scotch Lamb and Specially Selected Pork are a delight to prepare, cook and serve. By understanding a little more about meat quality and cooking methods, you can be sure you're making the most of these supremely versatile ingredients.

HOW TO CHECK THE QUALITY OF THE BEEF, LAMB OR PORK

The surest way to produce meals of excellent, consistent quality is to start with the best quality ingredients available. Meat is one of the key ingredients to 'get right' given its commanding position on a menu or as part of your cooking repertoire.

The fine quality and established provenance of meat from Scotland makes it a delight to cook and serve. Over the following pages, we will look at key factors to be aware of – meat colour, drip loss, lipid oxidation, storage and handling – that may affect meat eating quality during the kitchen stage.

The implications of drip loss

Drip loss is officially defined as:

1. The discharge of exudates (mainly water) from the carcase.

2. The loss of fluid from retail cuts whilst on display.

3. The loss of fluid from meat on thawing following freezing.

Essentially, 'drip' is a watery fluid which seeps from the cut ends of meat over time. Commercially, any weight lost as water by drip or evaporation has a repercussion on the bottom line – weight equals cost.

Lipid Oxidation (rancidity and off – flavours)

Fat is the other accomplice to myoglobin in affecting the odour, flavour and shelf life of fresh, frozen and cooked meat and meat products.

Information on fat and marbling can be found on pages 80-81.

Storage is key to working effectively with your meat.

The effect of various factors on the onset of oxidative rancidity in fat

FACTOR	EFFECT
Initiators	Oxidation is catalysed (i.e. accelerated) by heat (see below), light and iron (haem pigments)
Oxygen	Packaging that excludes oxygen, delays oxidation
Fatty acid composition	Beef and lamb are less likely to suffer from fatty acid oxidation because the fats they contain are more saturated and therefore more stable
Temperature	Higher temperatures increase oxidation
Antioxidant	Vitamin E is an antioxidant in meat. Occurs naturally in grass and can be added to animal feed to reduce oxidation
Comminution ('mixing')	Increases oxidation reducing shelf life
Cooked meat	Cooking speeds up oxidation. Free iron from heat denatured myoglobin acts as a catalyst

Source: Meat and Livestock Commission, British Nutrition Foundation 2004

Factors affecting weight loss in meat by drip and evaporation (and how to minimise them)

FACTOR	EFFECT	WHAT YOU CAN DO
Chilling rate	Considerate chilling reduces evaporative losses: cold shortening	Understand from your supplier(s) their chilling procedures – insist on considerate chilling
Pre-slaughter stress	Can lead to poor water retention/ high drip loss can ensue	Visit your abattoir; Scotch Beef and Scotch Lamb should undergo heavily monitored pre-slaughter checks to reduce stress levels
Meat pH	High pH meat (>pH 6.0) has low drip loss	Many factors involved (see Abattoir section)
Electrical stimulation	In conjunction with considerate chilling, Electrical Stimulation (ES) can reduce evaporation	Understand from your supplier(s) their procedures (see Abattoir section)
Size of meat pieces	Drip loss in joints and roasts are 10 times lower than in steaks and chops (due to surface area)	Understand the benefits to you and write specifications accordingly
Packaging	Pressure exerted on meat by tight fitting films can increase drip loss	Understand the implications to you and write specifications accordingly; speak to your butcher and see what other packaging methods could be used
Freezing and thawing	Drip loss can double as a result of freezing	Manage your deliveries to reduce the volume of meat that needs to be frozen; minimise non-blast (rapid) freezing, or freezing completely

Source: Meat and Livestock Commission

Commercially, any weight lost as water by drip or evaporation has a repercussion on the bottom line – weight equals cost.

Understanding meat colour

The exterior of the sirloin has turned bright red as the presence of oxygen in the air has changed the myoglobin to oxymyoglobin. The steak which has just been cut from the same sirloin shows how the interior colour of the meat is still in its purple-red state of non-oxygenated myoglobin.

This is discussed further on page 79.

MEAT MANAGEMENT IN THE KITCHEN

Knowledgeable handling and responsible preparation of meat are vital stages even before cooking commences. This section tells you how to look after your meat, and your customers.

Minced and chopped meats, rolled joints

'Proper' cooking requires the centre of the meat to reach a core temperature of at least 70°C for 2 minutes, or an equivalent, as follows:

Internal Meat Temperature	Duration
60°C	45 minutes
65°C	10 minutes
70°C	2 minutes
75°C	30 seconds
80°C	6 seconds

Note: due to the 'mixing' that inevitably happens to produce these products, bacteria have a greater likelihood of finding their way into the meat whereas intact joints are internally protected by the meat's surface.

Whole cuts or joints?

Whole cuts or joints of lamb and beef are traditionally served pink or rare. However, if the meat is pierced or on the bone, you should adhere to the table above. Of course, different dishes need different cooking times. If you work out the temperature and time you need to cook a particular dish in your oven, you can use these settings and times to cook the dish in the future.

Pork

It is a common misconception that pork must be fully cooked before it's served. This is not the case with pork being just as delicious served 'juicy' as it is fully cooked. A temperature probe is a useful way to check pork's core temperature. Stick to the internal meat temperature guidance opposite for a delicious result.

Reheating meat

When reheating meat, it needs to be piping hot all through and reach a core temperature of 82°C in Scotland (rest of UK 75°C). It should not be reheated a second time.

Play it cool

Once cooked, meat that is not going to be served should be cooled as fast as possible. The safest way is to divide it into smaller amounts in shallow dishes. It should not be 'forced' by refrigeration as this could warm up other food in the fridge.

Storing food (hot and chilled)

Temperature control is essential to prevent risk to health and there is also a legal obligation to keep to standard.

HOT
Hot food must be kept above 63°C.

CHILLED
Chilled food must be kept at or below 8°C: the coldest part of your fridge should be between 0°C and 5°C.

Whole cuts or joints of lamb and beef are traditionally served pink or rare.

More information can be found by logging onto www.food.gov.uk/scotland or by visiting www.eatwell.gov.uk

Is your fridge 8°C or below?

Storage advice

- Stick to fridge layouts – raw and ready-to-eat should never be stored together.
- Raw meat should be stored in a raw meat only fridge.
- Salamis and other charcuteries can be stored in a general fridge.
- In an operation where raw meat needs to share space with other items, it should always be at the bottom.
- Raw meat should be stored in containers so it cannot drip.
- Monitor your stock – overcrowding your fridge means it has to work really hard to keep things at the right temperature.

- Label with 'Use by' or 'Best before' and storage details ('Chilling required'). Use the first in, first out rule so that food with a shorter shelf life is used first and never use after the date has passed.
- Always check the labels – the time invested in sticking them on will be redundant otherwise.
- Read the supplier labels too – there could be some valuable information on them.
- If the packaging is opened or pierced in any way the information is no longer relevant.

Service and Display

Service and display is also a means of 'storing' food so avoiding risk of cross-contamination and inconsistent temperature control. The following guidelines must be ruthlessly applied when keeping food out of its temperature-controlled environment:

- Hot foods can be kept below 63°C for a maximum of two hours (and removed from their temperature controlled state only once).
- Chilled foods can be kept above 8°C for a maximum of four hours (and removed from their temperature controlled state only once).
- Separate raw and ready-to-eat foods in display and use separate utensils for handling product.

After these times have elapsed, the food should be thrown away or chilled as quickly and safely as possible until final use.

Cross-contamination

For the commercial chef, if your customers suffer from food poisoning after eating at your establishment, the consequences for your reputation and business could be devastating.

Cross-contamination is one of the major causes of food poisoning and should be avoided at all costs.

In an operation where raw meat needs to share space with other items, it should always be stored at the bottom.

 For further information please visit The Food Standards Agency website at *www.food.gov.uk*

COOKING – THE BIGGER PICTURE

In this section we look at simple cooking techniques to make the most of roasting and grilling. Cooking meat is simple, as long as you get the basics right – ingredients, "heat" and equipment.

Ingredients

- With meat, the importance of fat depends on you (or your customers') preference. When cooking steaks or roasts, a thin layer of fat enhances succulence and flavour. It also aids heat distribution through the meat. Excess fat can be trimmed prior to serving.

- To maximise browning, pat steaks, cubes and pot roasts, dry with kitchen paper before sealing over a high heat.

- If your meat has been vacuum-packed, drain thoroughly to remove excess moisture.

'Heat'

Obviously different cuts require different cooking methods. For example the tougher cuts benefit from being cooked at a moist, low heat.

- Do not pierce the meat during the cooking as piercing allows valuable juices to escape. When turning, use tongs, not a fork.

- Turn burgers with a spatula. Do not compress, this also forces out juices.

- Know your oven. Gas and electric cooking times are similar, but age and size of your oven can affect cooking times.

Equipment

- Good cooking utensils are essential. Pans should be thick enough to heat evenly and take the extreme temperatures of a commercial oven. Use the appropriate pan for the cut size.

- Non-stick pans are good when cooking with small amount of fat.

- To avoid excess fat when roasting, use a rack, but baste frequently to ensure heat consistency and great roasting flavours.

- Not sure of your oven? Check the temperature with an oven thermometer.

Tip: Use thermometers that are calibrated regularly.

A thin layer of fat benefits large cuts during roasting: you can trim after cooking if required. See marbling, pages 80 – 81, for more information.

RED MEAT COOKING ADVICE: ROASTS

Whichever method of cooking you choose, Scotch Beef, Scotch Lamb and Specially Selected Pork will deliver beyond your customers' expectations. By using different cuts from the animals, the accomplished chef can call on different cooking methods – but the standards of the meat will always be high.

But what better way to enjoy beef, lamb and pork than roasting? Regardless of advances and evolutions in cuisines and food, there is no doubt that the quintessential British dish is the Sunday roast!

Roasting

Roasting provides the catalyst to bring out the meat's attributes.

Maillard Reaction – the complex chemical reaction between protein and sugars which yields brown coloured products and aroma compounds on cooking, developing the flavour and colouring personalities of meat.

Gorgeous Scotch Lamb – a traditional dish is here contemporised by serving with roasted Mediterranean vegetables

The secret recipe for carving success

Ingredients: Your choice of:

Scotch Beef	Scotch Lamb	Specially Selected Pork
Topside	Rack	Shoulder
Top rump	Saddle, boned and rolled	Leg
Sirloin, boned and rolled	Shoulder, boned and rolled	Belly*
Rib eye		Loin
Sirloin, larder trimmed	Leg mini joints	Collar*
Sirloin, mini joints	Whole leg	
Fore rib, carvery cut		
Fore rib, oven prepared		
Leg of Mutton Cut	*May need previous preparation before roasting*	

Equipment:
- Carving knife, a good sharp one.
- Carving fork.
- Hygienic gloves (optional: if not available, thoroughly washed hands).
- Serving spoons.
- Scissors.
- Ladles.
- Serviettes.
- Hot plates.
- Steel/knife sharpener (partly for the theatre!)

Method:
- Start by browning the outside of the meat, either on the stove top or in the oven, at a high temperature, 220°C, for 15–20 minutes.
- Once the meat has been browned, lower the temperature to 130°C and complete the process so the food is tender on the inside.
- Serve and enjoy (and count the takings!)

 Use forequarter cuts like Brisket and LMC and make great savings to your bottom line.

ROASTING YIELD

Yield – namely the amount of cooked product produced (and 'used') from the uncooked product – can primarily be affected by two things, loss of weight during cooking and wastage in carving and serving.

Traditionally, there is a standard formula for cooking meat based on minutes per kilogramme or alternatively wait patiently, thermometer in hand. Both ways will cook your meat but also eat into potential profitability. The reason for this is that not all meat is the same.

Quality Meat Scotland recommends the recipe on page 39 that ensures very moist, flavour-rich meat. But here are the facts:

• 30–50% weight can be lost at the traditional 200°C or above that has always been deemed standard.

• the lower roasting temperature of 130°C offers a weight loss of just 14–25%.

The reason meat loses so much moisture at 200°C or above is simple. Meat can violently contract at high temperatures due to the denaturisation of the fibres. This action squeezes the meat and causes moisture to be lost. By cooking meat more gently, such violent reactions do not occur and so more moisture is retained in the meat and more 'weight' remains.

Different joints will have a different yield depending on cooking method and temperature. The following graphs demonstrate the differences. The second graph shows a slight increase in the yield of roasted sirloin which is cooked in a traditional oven rather than steam roasting.

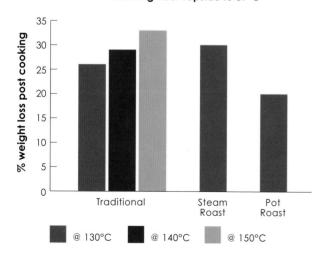

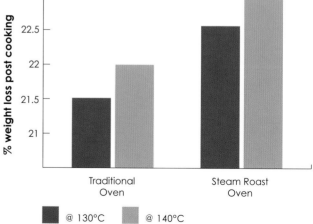

Source: Meat and Livestock Commission

 Cook lower and longer for larger yield!

Roast 'Doneness'

The formula for roasting meat is based on minutes spent in the oven per kilo of meat.

Weigh the piece of meat before cooking and calculate the cooking time. If you are roasting a stuffed joint – weigh after stuffing. Use a skewer to test the juices' colour to indicate what stage the meat is at.

Rare	Medium	Well done
Juices are red.	Juices are pink.	Juices are clear.
Internal temperature: 30 – 51°C.	Internal temperature: 63 – 68°C.	Internal temperature: 68 – 70°C.
Allow 15 – 20 minutes per 450g (1lb)	**Allow 22 – 25 minutes per 450g (1lb)**	**Allow 26 – 30 minutes per 450g (1lb)**

After the roast comes out of the oven, cover it with foil, (shiny side down) and allow it to rest for at least 10 – 15 minutes. This allows the meat to relax so the juices become evenly distributed throughout, making it more succulent and easier to carve.

 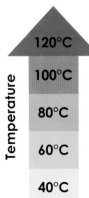

The effects of cooking temperature

Temperature

120°C — True Maillard reactions for desirable flavours and smells to make you feel hungry.

100°C — Contractile proteins harden, meat 'crisps.' Meat flavour develops.

80°C — Collagen begins gelatinisation, insoluble shrinks (toughening) and expresses water, pigment denatures, sticky 'goo' develops.

60°C — Coagulated protein can form exudate. Contractile proteins denature (toughening).

40°C

 Download our free "Perfect Steaks and Roasts" app for iPhone, iPod Touch and Android.

CARVING TECHNIQUES

Carving bone in joint

- Position the joint as shown, steadying it by inserting the prongs of the fork. The pelvic bone should be on the underside and the position of the bones will dictate the slices. Make the first cut by inserting the knife on the far side and cutting through to the bone, then levelling the knife to be almost parallel to the board.

- Make a second cut a little over ¼" to the left and by changing the knife to almost parallel with the bone, remove the first slice.

This is how it will look once you have carved as many as you can.

- Continue carving towards the knuckle, changing the angle for larger slices, removing after every 2 or 3.

- Turn over, steady with the fork and make a similar cut to the first cut you made, moving towards the knuckle as per the other side.

(Carvery Cut) Leg of lamb M.B.G. (Meat Buyers Guide) ref: 2051

Carving a roast

There are two methods of carving boned and rolled joints. Either lay the piece on its side and then cut slices from it almost as if it was a loaf of bread, or you may prefer to position it so that the round surface is horizontal and then carve across the grain.

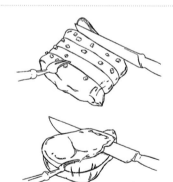

Place joint so that round surface is vertical and insert fork into curved side nearest to you or, if particularly long, it might be easier to insert nearer the middle and carve from the far end. When remaining piece is too thin and 'wobbly' to carve, lay it down so that the round surface is horizontal, inserting fork into side nearest to you and carve slices across the grain, increasing the angle as you come to the end.

Two tips for carving success:

- Always reduce the size of the cut to make carving easier.

- Always cut across the grain.

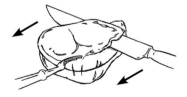

RED MEAT COOKING ADVICE: STEAKS/GRILLING

Steak remains one of the UK's most popular dishes. Your first step is to ask for Scotch when buying steaks – whether that be fillet, sirloin, T-bone or the less well known cuts on the following pages.

Pork steaks are known as loin steaks, chops, leg or shoulder steaks. The main cuts of lamb are cutlets, chops, valentine steaks and leg steaks.

The best way to cook great steak is on a grill / griddle, pre-heated to a high temperature. Quality Meat Scotland recommends the following 3 steps to great steak success:

01 Lightly coat the steak with oil before placing on a grill at a 45° angle.

02 Allow the meat to cook until the desired amount of browning occurs on the char marks, then rotate 45° to create a criss-cross effect on that side of the steak.

03 Turn the meat and repeat step 2 until the steak has been cooked to customer requirements. Remove, drain excess oil (should be minimal) dress the plate and get it on the pass.

It is important to ensure that all sides of any steak are sealed/subjected to sufficient heat to reduce to a safe level or kill harmful bacteria.

Which Beef steak?

Steak offers a good deal of flexibility for chefs of all standards in terms of size, flavour, depth and tenderness. The following guide is designed to help identify the differences available to you.

CUT	WHERE FROM	COOKED STEAK CHARACTERISTIC
Hindquarter		
Fillet	Loin	Lean and tender, light in flavour
Porterhouse	From rump end of loin	Large steak, very flavoursome, variation in tenderness
Rump	Rump or hip	Very flavoursome, fat on outer edge, variation in tenderness
Sirloin	Loin	Tender and full flavoured, good marbling on steak, fat on outer edge
T-bone	Lower end of the sirloin and fillet	Large T-shaped bone, combination of textures and flavours
Tournedos	Fillet from the loin	Lean and tender, light in flavour, fine textured
Forequarter		
Rib-eye	From the fore-rib/wing rib	High marbling content, tender and full flavoured
Chuck steak	From the shoulder/chuck	High marbling content, multi-muscled cut. Best suited to slow moist cooking. Tender and flavoursome
Rib cutlets	From the fore-rib/wing rib	High marbling content, tender and full flavoured, contains rib bone
LMC slices (part seamed)	Shoulder/top/thick rib	Very lean, fine textured, best suited to slow moist cooking
LMC (fully seamed)	Shoulder/top/thick rib	Best suited for sandwiches. Slice thinly and flash fry, very lean, fine textured
Feather steaks (part seamed)	Shoulder/top of blade	Best suited to slow moist cooking, tender and flavoursome
Feather steaks (fully seamed)	Shoulder/top of blade	Best suited to slow moist cooking, tender and flavoursome or quick cook rare
Blade steaks	Shoulder/top of blade	Slow moist cooking results in tender meat or quick cook rare
Under blade steaks	Shoulder/under blade	Very lean, fine textured
Brisket steaks	Breast/flank	Very lean and coarse grained. Light in flavour. Best suited to slow moist cooking
Brisket steak blocks	Breast/flank	Very lean and coarse grained. Light in flavour. Best suited to slow moist cooking
Shin/shank boneless	Fore leg	Very flavoursome, coarse texture, very high in collagen that gelatinises. Best suited to slow moist cooking
Shin/shank bone-in (Osso buco)	Fore leg	Very flavoursome, coarse texture, very high in collagen that gelatinises. Best suited to slow moist cooking

 For more information on forequarter steaks check page 51.

Rare steak safety guidance

A much debated industry theory suggests that rare steak is not safe – although the surface is cooked, the inside is not and so cannot be fit for consumption. A study was commissioned at The University of Nottingham by the Meat and Livestock Commission in November 2003 to investigate whether steak could be cooked rare because the cooking procedure killed all vegetative cells on the meat surface. **After significant testing, it was concluded that if recommended handling and cooking practices are followed and hygiene levels are respected, there is no risk involved in consumption of rare steak.**

The internal temperature of cooked steak is another indication of its 'doneness'. Beware that core temperature will depend on the temperature before cooking.

 When cooking 'Bleu', seal all six sides.

Beef Steak 'Doneness'

There are six traditionally accepted cooking specifications for steak. Lamb and pork are usually served well done or rosé (pink). The photographs show what each of these specifications should look like internally:

1 Bleu

There must be careful consideration and strict hygiene assessments given to steaks that are to be cooked so lightly. The meat should be seared and sealed on each of its six sides. The meat should be totally raw internally. To touch, it should feel like a raw piece of meat.

Internal temperature: 10-29°C

2 Rare

Ensure that each of the six sides has an equal quantity of cooking and the temperature is kept above 175°C. The steak should have a 5-8mm depth of fully cooked meat around the exterior and a raw interior. To touch, the steak will feel slight resistance and then totally raw.

Internal temperature: 30-51°C

3 Medium Rare

Cook this as for the rare steak but it may be advantageous to finish the cooking in an oven to avoid overcooking one of the sides. The meat should be considerably more cooked than the rare steak but have a very pink/reddish colour and be very moist. To touch, the meat will be slightly resistant with some 'give' in the middle.

Internal temperature: from 57°C to 63°C

For perfect steaks every time, download our free **"Perfect Steaks and Roasts"** app for iPhone, iPod Touch and Android.

 Chef Beware! Ensure tongs are washed at 82°C or above each time they are used to turn a steak to avoid cross contamination.

4 Medium

This can be cooked in the same way as the rare. The look of the steak will be less pink in the middle and should be moist, but have less colour. To touch, the steak will resist but still have a small amount of 'give'.

Internal temperature: 63-68°C

5 Medium Well

This steak should look cooked through with no hint of colour and a slight dryness around the exterior. The middle should still have a little moisture. To touch, it should be firm.

Internal temperature: 72-77°C

6 Well Done

The steak should look fully cooked and have no pinkness whatsoever. The meat colour should be shaded quite grey on the interior. To touch, it will be very firm.

Internal temperature: 77°C or above

QMS recently published a poster for chefs to understand the differences of cooking each method. To obtain a copy of the poster free of charge, simply contact the QMS office on 0131 472 4040 or email info@qmscotland.co.uk.

 These measurements should be used as a guide only.

STEAKS: MORE THAN FILLET AND SIRLOIN

Fillet, sirloin, rump – in recent times most chefs and catering professional have relied heavily on the hindquarter to deliver the majority of steak offerings on their menus. Great cuts of meat but how about the rest of the beast?

Ten Rib Forequarter Lateral

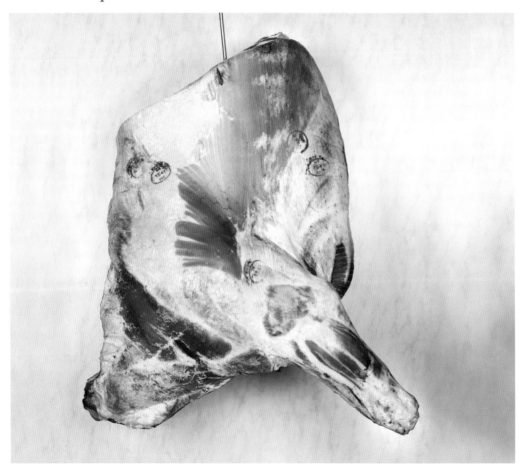

Relevant inspection stamps visible.

Slaughter plant number visible.

Consequently, unbalanced carcase utilisation has been prevalent and has prevented such beautiful cuts of meat such as onglet and blade of beef being presented on many of our foodservice menus. The forequarter offers some great opportunities to wow your customers (and it's very kind to the budget).

Ten Rib Forequarter Medial

Taken from 451kg carcase.

R4L grade, aged 10 days – Angus Crossbreed

- *clean rib and spinal column.*
- *discoloured neck meat (from 'sticking') to be removed.*

 For more information on forequarter usage email *info@qmscotland.co.uk*

Forequarter Primal Breakdown

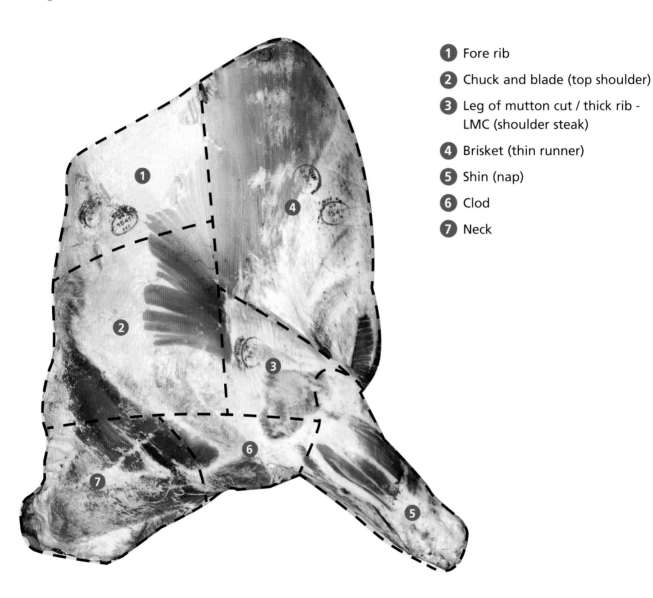

1. Fore rib
2. Chuck and blade (top shoulder)
3. Leg of mutton cut / thick rib - LMC (shoulder steak)
4. Brisket (thin runner)
5. Shin (nap)
6. Clod
7. Neck

i NOTE: Some cuts have different names in Scotland – these are shown in brackets.

The following sequence illustrates the versatility and easy manipulation of several forequarter muscles to achieve chef friendly meal solutions.

(3) LMC Steak Primal

(3) LMC Slices

Fully trimmed of all fat and connective tissue
• weight guide – 3-4kg

Sliced evenly to required portion weight
• weight guide – 300-500g, or as required
• cooking – braising, stewing, pot-roasting

(4) Brisket Muscle

(4) Brisket Steaks

(4) Brisket Steak Blocks

From brisket block, fully trimmed of all fat and connective tissue
• weight guide – 2-4kg

Divided into two equal portions prior to slicing into required portion steaks
Steaks slice laterally across grain
• weight guide – 180-240g
• cooking – braising, pot-roasting

Brisket muscle can be cut as block steaks
Diamond scored for penetration of marinades
• weight guide – 150-250g
• cooking – braising, pot-roasting

(1) Rib Cutlets

(1) Rib Eye

(2) Chuck Steaks

(5) Shin Steaks (Osso buco)

Prepared from fore rib
Fully chined and trimmed
• weight guide – 280-320g
• cooking – open texture muscle – grilling, frying, roasting, braising

Prepared from fore rib
• weight guide – 230-280g
• cooking – open texture muscle – grilling, frying, roasting, braising

Sliced from fully trimmed primal
• weight guide – 300-400g
• cooking – braising, pot-roasting

Fully trimmed muscles, bone in
• weight guide – 250-350g
• cooking – braising, pot-roasting

 NOTE: No traditional steaks are cut from **(6)** and **(7)** but they are excellent stewing and braising meats.

Shoulder Block Boneless - Exploded View

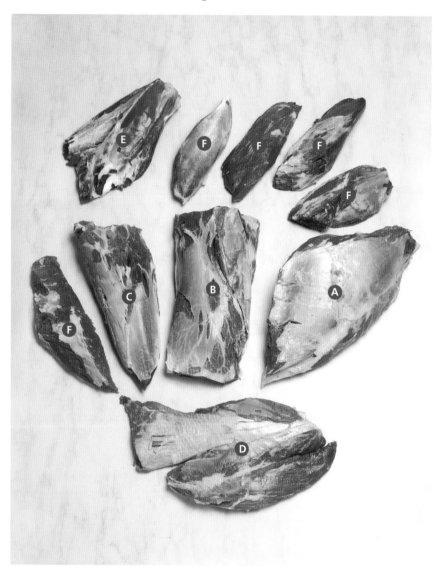

Untrimmed, seamed to individual muscle blocks/groups

A Leg of mutton cut

B Feather

C Blade

D Under blade muscle

E Shin muscle

F Clod

Shoulder Block Boneless
Bone removed, untrimmed internal view.

Shoulder Block Primal
Removed from forequarter following natural seams.

A LMC – Fully Seamed

- Trimmed of all visible fat and sinew, ready for slicing
- Weight guide – 1-2kg

LMC Steaks
- Fully trimmed, sliced to required weight and size
- Weight guide – 150-250g
- Cooking – braising, pot-roasting, frying

B Feather Muscle   ### B Feather Steaks

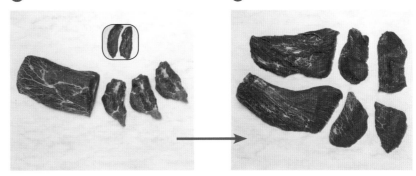

Feather Muscle
- Centre gristle removed
- Fully trimmed of external fat and gristle

Feather Steaks
- Sliced to required weight
- Cooking – frying, grilling, braising, pot-roasting

C Blade Muscle

- Fully trimmed of external fat and gristle prior to slicing
- Weight guide – 750g-1kg

Blade Steaks
- Sliced from blade muscle to required weight
- Weight guide – 180-230g
- Cooking – braising, pot-roasting

D Under Blade Muscle Steaks

- Fully trimmed of all fat, gristle and connective tissue
- Sliced across grain into required portions
- Cooking – frying, grilling, braising, pot-roasting

E Shin Boneless

- Steaked to required weights
- Weight guide – 180-240g
- Cooking – braising, pot-roasting

ACCOMPANIMENTS

	BEEF	LAMB	PORK		BEEF	LAMB	PORK
Almond		✓		Grape	✓		✓
Anchovy	✓	✓		Grapefruit			✓
Anise	✓	✓	✓	Haggis	✓	✓	✓
Apple			✓	Hard Cheese	✓		
Apricot		✓	✓	Horseradish	✓		
Artichoke (Globe)		✓	✓	Juniper	✓		✓
Artichoke (Jerusalem)	✓		✓	Lemon	✓	✓	
Aubergine		✓		Lime	✓		
Bacon	✓		✓	Liver	✓		
Beans		✓	✓	Mint	✓	✓	
Beetroot	✓		✓	Mushroom	✓		✓
Bell pepper	✓			Mustard	✓		
Blackberry	✓			Nutmeg		✓	
Black pudding	✓	✓	✓	Oily fish	✓		✓
Blue cheese	✓		✓	Olive	✓		
Broccoli	✓		✓	Onion	✓	✓	✓
Cabbage (s)	✓	✓	✓	Orange	✓		
Caper	✓	✓		Oyster	✓		✓
Cardamom		✓	✓	Parsley	✓	✓	✓
Carrot	✓			Parsnip	✓	✓	✓
Celery	✓	✓	✓	Pea	✓	✓	✓
Cherry		✓		Peanut	✓	✓	✓
Chestnut		✓	✓	Pear	✓		✓
Chilli	✓		✓	Pepper	✓	✓	✓
Cinnamon	✓	✓	✓	Pineapple			✓
Clove	✓		✓	Prune			✓
Cocoa	✓			Potato	✓	✓	✓
Coconut	✓		✓	Rhubarb		✓	✓
Coffee	✓		✓	Rosemary		✓	✓
Coriander leaf		✓	✓	Saffron	✓	✓	
Coriander seed			✓	Sage			✓
Courgette	✓	✓	✓	Shellfish	✓	✓	✓
Cucumber	✓	✓	✓	Swede	✓	✓	✓
Cumin		✓	✓	Thyme	✓	✓	✓
Dill	✓	✓	✓	Tea	✓	✓	✓
Egg	✓		✓	Tomato	✓	✓	✓
French beans	✓		✓	Truffle	✓		✓
Foie gras	✓		✓	Turnips	✓	✓	✓
Garlic	✓	✓	✓	Walnut	✓		
Ginger	✓		✓	Watercress	✓		✓
Goat cheese		✓		Watermelon			✓

CLASSIC BEEF ACCOMPANIMENTS

Beef and horseradish, steak and ale pie, boiled beef and onions – such classic dishes have been around for centuries.

Marinate

What it does – adds flavour.

What to do – mix marinade ingredients. Place meat and marinade in a plastic bag. Refrigerate.

What to use – horseradish, mustard, red wine, peppercorns, garlic, ginger, wholegrain mustard, brown sugar, allspice, cumin, paprika, wasabi paste, chilli, garlic salt.

Glaze

What it does – adds flavour, enhances visual appeal of cooked meat.

What to do – brush the glaze over the meat a few minutes before end of cooking.

What to use – sugar is essential for glazing. So try blackbean glaze, barbecue sauce or a sweetened wasabi and horseradish.

Accompaniments for Beef

What they do – enhance the meat's natural flavours, enriching each other and the eating experience.

What to do – combine the ingredients and serve with your beef dish.

What to use – for creamy blue cheese, combine natural yoghurt with a good blue vein cheese and chopped spring onions. For a hot chilli accompaniment, mix natural yoghurt, tomatoes and chillis. For the best of British, make some Yorkshire puddings and gravy and serve with horseradish and peppery watercress sauce.

Get boozy! Beef laps up stouts so add your favourite ales in pies and casseroles. Or pan fry and deglaze with Madeira. You can even poach fillet steaks in good red wine and serve with pomme purée and green beans!

Veal

There is a growing consumer interest for veal, it is from younger animals and therefore the flavour is more discrete. There are two types of veal – veal and rosie veal.

COMPLEMENTING YOUR LAMB

Many chefs see lamb as an expensive choice. Yet lamb offers as many dish opportunities as beef, while suiting any budget. Scotch Lamb is quick to cook, tender and succulent. When correctly specified and trimmed it also offers a healthy option.

Roast lamb is a great favourite and offers a number of options – leg and shoulder joints, on the bone or boneless and rolled for easy carving. Rack of lamb always looks impressive. Here are our tips on how to make the most of Scotch Lamb.

- Choose your joint carefully – if you're not confident with carving, ask your butcher for a boned and rolled leg joint.

- Remove the joint from the packaging and pat dry with kitchen paper to absorb any juices. Seal the meat at a high heat in a frying pan to trigger the maillard reaction. Roast on a trivet with roasting vegetables and lamb bones in the roasting pan for a traditional jus.

- Don't forget to baste and turn the joint every 20 minutes. Avoid piercing the meat during cooking.

Try these fabulous ideas to make your lamb even tastier and more appealing to your customers:

Marinate

What it does – adds flavour.

What to do – mix marinade. Place meat and marinade in a plastic bag. Refrigerate.

What to use – curry paste, yoghurt and freshly chopped spring onion.

Glaze

What it does – adds flavour, enhances visual appeal of cooked meat.

What to do – brush the glaze over the meat a couple of minutes before end of cooking.

What to use – sugar is essential for glazing, so try redcurrant or mint jelly, curry paste or your best taco sauce!

Accompaniments for lamb

What they do – enhance the meat's natural flavours, enriching each other and the eating experience.

What to do – use these great combinations to make your Scotch Lamb a real winner.

What to use – slivers of garlic, sprigs of rosemary and/or anchovies can be pushed into slits cut in the meat. Try grinding grated lemon rind, root ginger and garlic, or mint and rosemary, into a paste to fill the slits. Serve with mint sauce and red wine gravy for a delicious dish.

Bake with aubergines, tomatoes, courgettes, olives and garlic for a Mediterranean twist. Or pot roast with root vegetables or butternut squash and red onions.

Flavoured butters also work well with lamb steaks and chops. Make by simply softening butter and folding through the grated rind of a lemon or lime, some thyme and rosemary. Or try some chilli paste and a few leaves of freshly torn basil.

In the 'pink'

Although it's your personal preference (or that of your customers), lamb should be served pink wherever possible. The principles of 'doneness' for lamb are the same as steak. To be absolutely sure, check the internal temperatures with a meat thermometer and use the steak guidelines on pages 46 – 47.

More to it than mint: Lamb has the ability to work so well with many ingredients.

Chefs' myth

Resting allows the juices to go back into the meat… WRONG! Meat loses moisture as it cools. Try it for yourself – weigh a piece of meat just after you take it out from the oven… wait 20 minutes and then weigh it again. Weight after will be less than the 'just after' weight. Only texture will improve slightly after resting and the red 'doneness' is less apparent.

Mutton

For centuries, mutton has been a significant part of the diet in many European countries and it does indeed make excellent eating. Here's a guide to some lesser known terms:

Mutton: meat from the carcase of an older sheep, especially that of a mature sheep.

Hogg or hogget: (i) young sheep (male or female), slaughtered before any permanent teeth have erupted. The classification scheme terms hoggets as old season's lambs; (ii) a live sheep between the time of weaning and its first shearing.

Mutton can be prepared in the same way as lamb using the recommended guidelines. When choosing your dish and cooking style, bear in mind that some sinews may be more overdeveloped than for lamb – a result of age – which does suggest that slower, 'moist' cooking styles are preferable.

Talk to your butcher about whether he can supply quality mutton from Scotland and the cuts and cooking methods he recommends.

Source: Danish Meat Research Institute

Mutton is becoming a popular meat amongst even the most decorated chefs.

Source: Mark Hix, Caprice Holdings, 'An abundance of rare ideas'

 For more information and recipe inspiration, log onto *www.scotchbeefandlamb.com*

CLASSIC PORK ACCOMPANIMENTS

Depending on the cut and level of fat cover, pork generally enjoys a relatively light flavour. Fresh pork is also a product which adapts very easily to a range of marinades and quick cooking techniques and is therefore very popular for Eastern cuisine. Perhaps Britain's favourite, however, is a slow roasted loin of pork – complete with crispy crackling and apple sauce.

Crackling

For the perfect crackling, you need to ensure the skin of pork is scored well using a very sharp knife – or Stanley knife. Creating diamond shapes across the skin will allow you to enjoy bite-sized pieces later on. Before placing in the oven, ensure the skin has plenty of salt rubbed across the scored lines. This helps dry the crackling out and adds to its deliciously crispy nature. When roasting pork, always have the skin to the top.

You can always check when pork is cooked by inserting a skewer to the thickest part of the joint. The juices which come out should run clear – i.e. with no pink traces. Always allow the joint to rest or relax sufficiently once it's been removed from the oven.

Accompaniments – not just apple!

There are so many spices and seasonings which work well with all sizes of fresh pork products from the larger joints to the smaller chops, steaks and medallions. Instead of relying on apple on the side, why not consider other accompaniments such as peach, apricot, or pineapple. Herbs love pork with sage, rosemary and thyme working well across the wide range of pork cuts available.

Marinades

A fantastic way to introduce added flavour to pork, marinades also help limit the meat from drying out by keeping it moist and succulent. The list of opportunities are endless but why not try working with combinations including soy sauce, honey, lemon, vinegar, fresh herbs and spices. Caribbean and Eastern cuisines use marinades a great deal to impart their legendary flavour and textures. Remember to plan in advance giving the pork a minimum of 2 hours marinating before cooking.

OFFAL – NOT A THING OF THE PAST

Recent research undertaken by QMS identifies opportunities for meat products termed 'offal'. Despite a decline in sales of offal towards the latter part of the 20th Century, today's shopper is increasingly looking for value-for-money products – but is unwilling to compromise on the standards offered by the Scotch and Specially Selected brands, particularly in relation to areas such as approved animal feed and high animal health and welfare.

Although offal products may not be to everyone's tastes, there is also a growing awareness of the importance of good nutrition, and offal provides a very strong source of iron, vitamins A, D and C which are easily absorbed by the body.

Use of offal is not only economical but also environmentally friendly. We should use every part of the animal as it used to be. Haggis, trotters, black pudding and ox tail have a long tradition and are a good base for gastronomic creations.

Preparation styles offer great flexibility including grilling, frying, casseroling and braising, making offal a versatile addition to your repertoire. Talk to your butcher about the variety of offal available, and remember that Scotch Beef, Scotch Lamb and Specially Selected Pork offal products carry the same assured status as the premium cuts on the market.

Edible Offal

By law, the parts of cattle and sheep most likely to carry BSE must be removed. These parts are known as Specified Risk Material (SRM) and include brain and spinal cord. See Abattoir section page 92.

However, the following offal has been deemed edible and gives a wide range of flavours and cooking opportunities – offal is also a fantastic way of offering high gross profit dishes!

LAMB	BEEF	PORK
Heart	Kidney	Kidney
Lungs	Liver	Liver
Sweetbread	Lungs	Lungs
Testicles	Heart	Heart
Pancreas	Pancreas	Pancreas
Kidney	Sweetbread	Sweetbread
Liver	Tongue	Tongue
Tongue	Cheek	Cheek
Casings	Tripe	Tripe
	Tail	Head
	Testicles	

Steak and Kidney pie – one of the 'school dinner' classics now on so many fine dining menus.

Source: Meat Hygiene Service

 For more information, log onto *www.food.gov.uk/scotland*

SUPPLY CHAIN FOCUS
NO COMPROMISE

The variety of Scotch Beef, Scotch Lamb and Specially Selected Pork cuts available means that no catering facility needs to compromise on red meat quality. Careful planning, the right butchery specifications and yield-efficient preparations enable the cost sector caterer to satisfy thousands of hungry students, visitors and staff, every day.

In an institutional catering environment such as a large university, the Group Executive Chef is responsible for a number of brigades that manage their own outlet on the site. These outlets can often range from a 24/7 snack proposition to silver service dining, meetings and conferences.

The businesses therefore need to operate independently and satisfy different eating occasions whilst maintaining the institution's overall high standards, profitability targets and consumer quality demands.

In large scale catering – often up to 800 or more diners in one sitting – Scotch red meat products are popular and reliable ingredients which the chefs agree do not have to be 'worked' hard to produce a great dish.

" Marbling's important. It looks good before you cook it but also keeps it moist, great for cook chill."

Graham Crump

In order to meet such large-scale demand, a central production unit (CPU) is often the most efficient solution. The CPU's cook chill system typically works on a four-day pattern:

Day 1 – butchers prepare to specification.

Day 2 – delivery to CPU, caged by 'batch'.

Day 3 – batch cooking, blast chilled within 90 minutes, kept in holding fridge.

Day 4 – delivered to unit, reheated and consumed.

To facilitate ordering and planning the process often works to a 10-week menu cycle.

Scotch Beef and Scotch Lamb more than satisfy the quality and consistency requirements of even the largest scale catering operations.

Scotch Beef and Scotch Lamb are available across the UK from all reputable catering and retail butchers supplying the catering trade.

Preparation is simplified by providing user-friendly specifications to the butcher. For example, specify 5kg bags of Scotch mince – to make six trays of twenty portions of lasagne (120 portions in all), requires 20kg of Scotch mince. So four bags need to be ordered. This eliminates the need to pre-weigh the mince and minimises wastage.

" For our blade of beef, we braise it gently for four to five hours and let it cool. It's then seared to colour and sliced into portions. We get about five or six portions out of the blade and we'll serve it with a red wine jus."
Graham Crump

Relations with the catering butcher are just as important for the cost sector as the profit sector. With such high annual red meat usage, butchers are required to tender for business, meeting specification, volume, pricing, invoicing and delivery criteria. A good catering butcher will liaise with the units recommending ideas, new and innovative cuts (at the right price) and offer in house butchery training to the brigades.

To keep within budget, the forequarter of Scotch Beef offers a number of profitable and delicious meal solutions. Blade of Scotch Beef can be gently braised and served with caramelised button onions and a red wine jus for special occasions, or simply braised and served on creamed potato. Likewise, shoulder of

Scotch Lamb can be double roasted to extract maximum flavour at a good price point.

Scotch Beef makes great mince and dice, the foundations of many batch-cooked, cost-sensitive meals. For the cook chill process, the propensity for marbling in Scotch Beef and Scotch Lamb ensures that the meat will remain moist. Good butchers will even search out the best marbled cuts if this information is on the specification.

The other ally of the cost sector caterer is 'yield'. Quality Meat Scotland's recommended cooking practices counter the price premium of Scotch Beef and Scotch Lamb. The integrity and care that has gone into producing meat for a carvery roast ensures that the meat served is flavoursome, moist and a delight to the customers – for more formal dinners Scotch sirloin and Scotch rib of beef are ideal, or for a lower cost, Scotch topside of beef.

Quality Meat Scotland supports the cost sector catering industry by providing information and assists chefs by hosting guided visits to abattoirs, farms and butchers.

With thanks to Graham Crump, Group Executive Chef and Amanda Simpson of the University of Warwick.

No. 3
BUTCHER

The best butchers and catering professionals provide a consistent and reliable service and excellent quality of meat. Many butchers are armed with exquisite skills and knowledge which have been passed down from generations. Some Scottish processors deliver directly to the foodservices. What's more, they provide an experience and environment which is valued by their customers – giving them a distinct advantage over their competition. If you are a consumer or a professional chef, check our list of butchers and suppliers on the Scotch Beef Club website (page 118).

A TRUSTED AND KNOWLEDGEABLE SUPPLIER:
CUT INFORMATION

A good relationship with an experienced butcher is fundamental to sourcing the best quality meat.

A recent butchery technique which has grown in popularity in the UK is that of 'seam' butchery. The process involves breaking down the carcase using nature's natural 'seams' between the muscles as the guides for cutting, rather than cutting across one or more muscles to produce a joint of meat. The cuts produced from seam butchery consist of single muscles. As they don't contain a range of muscles which cook at different times, the aim of seam butchery is to prevent uneven cooking – allowing for a more consistent end-result in the kitchen. More steaks are made available for grilling or frying and fewer cuts for stewing or pot roasting. Meat is put to better use with increased yields and less wastage all round.

The quality or standard of many restaurants is underpinned by the quality and origin of their meat. Restaurants require a catering butcher who can deliver products to a set of specifications which are consistent in weight, shape and quality. The catering butcher is not only an expert on the beef, lamb and pork carcase and available cuts, they're also extremely knowledgeable on competencies such as cutting, packing and ageing as well as health and safety requirements prior to their accreditation. This requires significant investment in staff over a number of years and business relationships are often in place over a long-term, allowing for greater collaboration between chef and butcher.

In this first section, we explore the wide range of Scotch Beef, Scotch Lamb and Specially Selected Pork cuts which your butcher can supply.

The versatility of Scotch Beef is as infinite as your imagination

Due to the variety of cuts that Scotch Beef offers, the range of possibilities you can offer your customer is huge. However, because of this very flexibility, all beef is not the same: different cuts require different treatment. The information opposite is a comprehensive snapshot of the most commonly used and prepared cuts.

SCOTCH BEEF FOREQUARTER CUTS

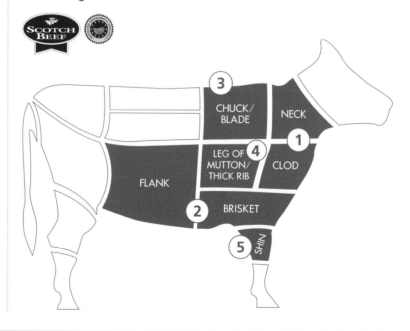

① Neck and clod

PRODUCTS: Diced.

COOKING METHODS: Stewing, casseroling, braising.

As a result of being heavily exercised, the neck and shoulder area of the animal comprise a range of intricate muscles, rich in collagen and full of flavour. Generally they are cheaper cuts of meat as there is a reasonable amount of fat and connective tissue throughout. For best results, it is recommended to cook slowly with plenty of moisture.

④ Leg of mutton / thick rib

PRODUCTS: Diced, steaks (thinly sliced and served rare only to avoid poor eating experience).

COOKING METHODS: Frying, stewing, grilling, casseroling.

This unusual cut is gaining in popularity. Located inside the shoulder, once fully seamed, the leg of mutton cut is lean, fine textured and full of flavour. Cut thinly, it's ideal for frying but it's always best not to overcook as it will dry out and become tough very quickly.

② Flank / brisket

PRODUCTS: Flank steak, roasting joints, short ribs.

COOKING METHODS: Ideal for moist, slow heat including stewing, braising and pot-roasting. Also excellent for curing.

The flank is cut from the animals stomach muscles. It's long, flat and very flavoursome. As a result of being a well exercised part of the animal, this muscle has an array of fibres and connective tissues. Steaks from the flank must be served rare or should employ alternative, slower cooking techniques.

Brisket is located further forward and, like flank, has a lot of texture and reasonable fat cover. It works well with moist slow heat and is excellent for curing.

③ Chuck / blade

PRODUCTS: Roasting joints and steaks when properly trimmed.

COOKING METHODS: Ideal for slow cooking such as casseroling, pot-roasting, braising and slow roasting.

The many different muscles in the shoulder contain a lot of connective tissues. As a result of so many muscles, the chuck and blade has varying degrees of tenderness and marbling.

Popular for marinating, it's also good for mincing as a result of the balance between flavoursome beef and fat content.

The feather muscle (feather blade) originates from this area, and is so called because of the heavy veining of connective tissue running up the middle. When cooked slowly, this gives a gelatinous consistency much loved by chefs.

⑤ Shin

PRODUCTS: Stock, stewing, casserole. (Ideal for osso buco)

COOKING METHODS: Stewing, casseroling.

The end of the animal's front legs, the shin is generally inexpensive. It should be given plenty of time to cook slowly and can be obtained either on or off the bone. Foodies particularly enjoy the marrow in the bone - a very Continental delicacy.

SCOTCH BEEF HINDQUARTER CUTS

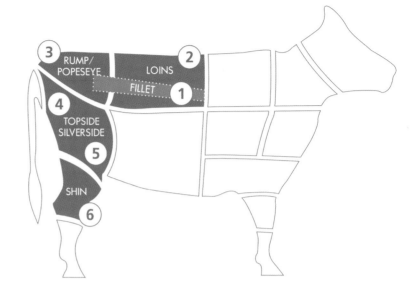

Classique Bistro Steaks

All these steaks need to be cooked quickly on high heat and served rare.

1. Onglet

– also known as thick skirt/flank on hanger steak. It is hung from the diaphragm between the kidneys.

2. Bavette Flanchet

– the extension of the flank.

3. Bavette Aloyau

– flat muscle from the animal side.

4. Picanha

– also known as rump cap or rump cover.

5. Iron flat steak

– also known as butcher's steak (see blade steak page 65).

① Fillet

PRODUCTS: Cut into steaks or roasted whole.

COOKING METHODS: Fillet trimmings from the head, tail or chain are great for stir frying or stroganoff. Add slivers to make tasty Thai beef soups.

Less than 1% of the carcase but always the most expensive. The fillet is the least exercised muscle of the animal and is known for its tenderness. It is also known as tenderloin or the undercut of the sirloin. It weighs approximately 2 – 2.5 kgs and is made up of the head, the canon and the tail. The fillet can be supplied with or without the "chain" muscle attached.

② Loin

PRODUCTS: The loin is made up of various ribs which are well known as steaks e.g. sirloin, T-bone, porterhouse etc. Sirloin steak left on the bone with fillet attached is called T-bone and sirloin left on the bone but without the fillet is called L bone. Loin cuts from the hindquarter begin from between the 10th and 11th rib. Rib eye is a forequarter cut taken from the fore rib, between the 6th and 10th ribs.

COOKING METHODS: Cuts from the loin offer a good deal of flexibility in terms of size, flavour and tenderness but all generally are suitable for higher temperature methods of cooking such as pan frying, grilling or roasting.

(3) Rump / popeseye

PRODUCTS: Roasting joints or sliced into steaks. Trimmed rump is also called D rump. Pave (French for paving stone and referring only to the shape) – is often used to describe a trimmed piece of rump that is very uniform and rectangular in shape.

COOKING METHODS: Rump is made up of three very different muscles – rump cap, rump heart (or eye) and rump tail. These muscles do vary in tenderness so seam butchery can improve consistency. These cuts can be cooked as roasts or sliced into high quality steaks. Rump heart being the tenderest. The cap (or cover), which is least tender, is often served in some countries as picanha.

(5) Silverside

PRODUCTS: Roasting and curing in joints of various sizes. Generally the Silverside is either cross cut into two joints or rolled whole. The "Salmon Cut" muscle can be removed from the main muscle by following a natural seam.

COOKING METHODS: Silverside is another slow cooking or carvery joint. It is very lean and sometimes has a layer of pre-formed fat added to prevent the meat becoming too dry during cooking.

Silverside is ideal for curing or salting. This can be either wet or dry curing using salt and a mixture of spices.

(4) Topside

PRODUCTS: Roasting joints of various sizes.

COOKING METHODS: Topside is generally roasted. Suitable for either dry or wet roasting.

Topside can be served whole, rolled, cap on or off. When fully trimmed, there is not much surface or intra muscular fat, so topside should be cooked medium to medium rare to remain moist. If the joint is to be cooked well done a longer slower method will be better.

To improve the yield from larger roasting joints roast at a lower temperature for longer. Reducing the cooking temperature to 130°C will reduce weight loss to between 15 – 25%.

(6) Shin

PRODUCTS: Hough and shin.

COOKING METHODS: Stewing, casseroling or confit.

Shin, also known as leg of beef in England, is rich in collagen and connective tissue and has delicious marrow running through the hollow centre of the bone. It is essential to cook slowly at lower temperatures with plenty of moisture that will make a rich tasty sauce. Cut right through the bone, it is perfect for Osso buco.

Cook slowly on or off the bone until the meat falls away and press into a mould to make traditional Scottish potted hough.

SCOTCH LAMB – TENDER AND TRADITIONAL

Scotch Lamb is a seasonal dish – at its very best during the late summer months and Autumn following the Spring lambing period. Fewer shoppers in Scotland consume lamb – compared with other areas of the UK. To help generate more interest and awareness of the product, QMS has undertaken a number of campaigns to promote this tender, traditional product to the industry's benefit.

Despite its image as a more expensive or fatty product, there are opportunities to source very economical cuts of Scotch Lamb which offer a range of taste experiences. When combined with complementary ingredients and flavours, and cooked in the most respectful way, the experience is sublime.

'…one of the most versatile meats…full of flavour and texture.'

Willi Elsener, Development Chef

'The flavour and succulence and light textured flesh make it ideal for all occasions.'

Marjan Lesnik, Development Chef

'…very delicate, sumptuous flavours…its inherent versatility; consistent quality and superb texture.'

Tony O'Reilly, Development Chef

① Leg

PRODUCTS: Joints, steaks, strips.

COOKING METHODS: Roast, pot roast, pan fry, stir-fry, grill, bbq, stew.

Leg of lamb is extremely well known and lends itself to a number of delicious products. It can be roasted bone-in or boned, rolled and tied with a stuffing of your choice. Alternatively, of course, you can source Scotch Lamb leg steaks which offer a quick to prepare dish for any menu. Steaks can be grilled/pan fried whole or cut into strips for a stir fry.

② Shoulder

PRODUCTS: Joints, steaks, diced (for stewing), mince.

COOKING METHODS: Roast, pot roast, pan fry, grill, bbq, stew.

The shoulder joint is another popular option for chefs as it's truly versatile. Comprising several different muscles, the shoulder should be cooked slower and longer than leg joints for a tender result. Diced products could be marinated and skewered. The shoulder is also an alternative source of steaks, again it would be better to marinade or cook more slowly. Lamb shoulder contributes approximately 24% of the carcase yield.

SCOTCH LAMB CUTS

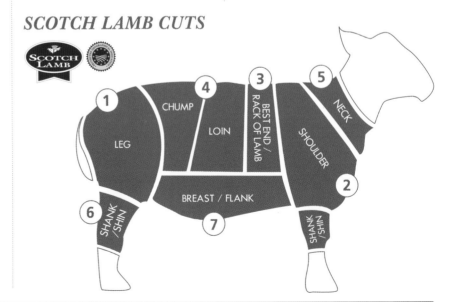

③ Best end / rack of lamb

PRODUCTS: Joints, cutlets, noisettes.
COOKING METHODS: Roast, pan fry, grill, bbq.

The best end is the joint between the neck and loin comprising the first eight ribs and the lean meat between them. A versatile cut, it can be prepared in a number of ways. It can be cut into little chops known as cutlets. Alternatively, the rack of lamb is the ultimate roasting joint for lamb lovers. If the animal's two racks of lamb are left joined together, butchers sometimes form a circle before trimming to create a spectacular crown roast.

④ Chump and loin

PRODUCTS: Joints, steaks, noisettes, chops, canon.
COOKING METHODS: Roast, pan fry, grill, bbq.

Loins can be roasted but are more commonly available as quick cooking cuts for the eager chef. Compared with other parts of the animal, loin cuts can be very lean. The eye of the loin can be trimmed of all fat and treated as a mini fillet. In this sense, the steaks are referred to as 'noisettes'. Most commonly, however, the loin is used for small steaks. Double Loin chops usually contain sections of both the loin and the fillet section.

⑤ Neck

PRODUCTS: Joints, dice.
COOKING METHODS: Stew, casserole, slow braising.

The muscles in the neck tend to be tougher than other cuts because they do more work. However, when cooked slowly, they produce a deliciously tender and tasty product. Ideal for diced products, lamb neck provides fantastic meat for stews and curries and is well known in countries that love lamb.

⑥ Shank and shin

PRODUCTS: Joints.
COOKING METHODS: Braise, casserole.

Lamb shanks are fairly lean and should be slow cooked whenever possible to allow the strands of meat to come apart easily. Packed full of flavour, the shanks have a rich texture. Hindshanks are larger and meatier than foreshanks although in some cases, butchers will include these in the leg as standard.

⑦ Breast / flank

PRODUCTS: Joints, mince.
COOKING METHODS: Braise, casserole, slow roast.

Often underused, the breast contributes around 14% of carcase volume. It's cost effective and can be supplied bone-in or boned. Generally used most with a stuffing – slow roasted.

SPECIALLY SELECTED PORK – A MODERN PRODUCT

As one of the world's favourite meats, pork has a special place in the heart of the keen chef. It's extremely versatile and fantastic value for money. In recent years, it has undoubtedly become more fashionable – perhaps helped by the fairly recent introduction of celebrity chef culture.

When dealing with pork in the kitchen, the keen chef must always respect the cooking temperature and time to avoid the meat drying out. It's packed full of flavour with a generous fat cover which excels during slower cooking methods – with some cuts still working very well at higher temperatures for frying and grilling.

Don't forget that pork is perfect for manufacturing a range of Britain's best loved meat products including bacons, hams and sausages which can all be endorsed to the high standards of Scotland's pig sector.

① Neck and shoulder

PRODUCTS: Joints, shoulder steaks, mince, sausages, diced (for casseroles).

COOKING METHODS: Roast, pot roast, pan fry, grill, bbq, stew, soup, broth.

The neck or collar as it is sometimes referred, produces delicious meat which should be slow cooked wherever possible to allow intramuscular fat to melt - keeping the meat moist and tender. Pork shoulder cuts are diverse and can be roasted, used for steaks, diced or minced. The shoulder cut alone contributes over 14% to the overall carcase volume.

② Loin

PRODUCTS: Joints, loin steaks, back bacon.

COOKING METHODS: Roast, pan fry, grill, bbq.

Loin chops and steaks contribute over 22% of the carcase volume. The loin delivers a number of roasting cuts with joints available both on and off the bone. Alternatively, the loin is used for deliciously lean chops and steaks - available with the rind on or off. The fillet (or tenderloin) of pork is the delicate, lean piece of meat which runs through the loin. Cured, the loin will give you back bacon.

SPECIALLY SELECTED PORK CUTS

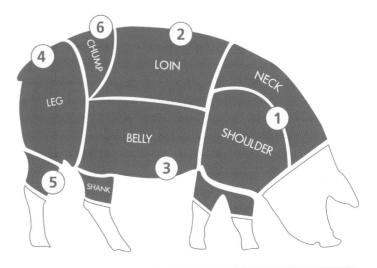

③ Belly / Flank

PRODUCTS: Joints, steaks, mince, sausages, bacon, spare-ribs.
COOKING METHODS: Roast, pot roast, pan fry, grill, bbq.

Pork belly is an increasingly fashionable product to work with and offers versatile cuts for all standards of chefs. Ribs can be marinated in a delicious sauce, belly can be rolled, tied and oven roasted or alternatively, sliced or cut into cubes. Cuts from the belly are fatty and as such offer great taste and beautifully tender meat. Alternatively, belly of pork is cured to make streaky bacon.

④ Leg

PRODUCTS: Joints, leg steaks, escallopes, diced (for kebabs).
COOKING METHODS: Roast, pot roast, pan fry, grill, bbq.

A vast number of legs of pork go for curing to make hams. Those that don't are dressed as fresh pork - cuts include leg steaks and roasting joints (which can be on the bone or boned, rolled and tied). The leg is a lean piece of meat so be careful not to dry it out when cooking. Legs contribute approximately 22% of the total pork carcase volume.

⑤ Knuckle / shank end

PRODUCTS: Joints, mince.
COOKING METHODS: Roast, pot roast.

Pork shank is the lower part of the leg. It is usually prepared by pot-roasting or oven-roasting slowly to retain the meat's tenderness. Shank is generally a cost efficient cut and can add something very different to your menu.

⑥ Chump

PRODUCTS: Hough and shin.
COOKING METHODS: Stewing, casseroling or confit.

Shin, also known as leg of beef in England, is rich in collagen and connective tissue and has delicious marrow running through the hollow centre of the bone. It is essential to cook slowly at lower temperatures with plenty of moisture that will make a rich tasty sauce. Cut right through the bone, it is perfect for Osso Bucco.

Cook slowly on or off the bone until the meat falls away and press into a mould to make traditional Scottish potted hough.

THE IMPORTANCE OF PACKAGING

The modern butcher supplies meat to his customers in a variety of ways – all of which have an effect on the meat (both beneficial and detrimental). For caterers, it is key to understand the options available to help specify their requirements clearly and correctly. Shelf-life is a key factor in meat storage and usage. Let's examine the options which a butcher may utilise.

1. Vacuum Packing

What is it?

- Seals cuts of meat in plastic bags from which air has been excluded.
- Extremely hygienic – packs are leakproof and 'clean.'

How does it work?

- The bags minimise both gas and moisture permeability, thereby acting as a barrier preventing the meat surface coming into contact with external oxygen and the meat's moisture from reaching the outside world.
- The lack of oxygen is enough to inhibit any Pseudomonads (bacteria which would cause the meat to deteriorate).

Tips

- Ask how quickly meat is vacuum packed post slaughter. Ensure this is as soon as possible to maximise shelf life or as long as possible after slaughter if you prefer the meat to be dry aged.
- Understand the quality of the vacuum packs themselves. Inferior quality materials can cause surface discolouration of the meat.
- Ensure a bone guard is used to prevent puncturing the membrane.

Be aware of…

- Sour or cheesy odours – when objectionable spoilage takes over.
- Colour change of the meat to 'bright red' on opening the pack through oxidation.
- Meat sitting in an excessive pool of its blood.

Note: some butchers do not like to vacuum pack because of claims that there is a 'sour' taste to the meat.

The film used in vacuum packaging ensures hygiene and a barrier to bacteria.

Check with your supplier what type of film they use.

Source: Meat and Livestock Commission, Shelf Life of Fresh Meat.

Storage Recommendations

DURATION	PACKAGING TYPE	RATIONALE
Short term (< 2 weeks)	Lower barrier vacuum packaging is sufficient	Cheaper; organism activity not a significant threat
Medium term (< 4 weeks)	High barrier film may be required and/or CO_2 flushed outer packaging	Requirement to reduce longer term storage consequences
Long term (2–4 months)	Top of the range non-permeable packaging and/or CO_2 flushing	Greater need to reduce longer term storage consequences

2. Overwrapping and Modified Atmosphere Packing

a. Overwrapping

What is it?

- Before modified atmosphere packaging and centralised pre-packing, overwrapping was extensively used for the retail display of meat.
- The film used for overwrapping is purposely permeable to external air.

How does it work?

- The film facilitates oxygenation of the meat, causing the production of oxymyoglobin and the red 'fresh meat' that consumers tend to look for.
- However, the meat soon oxidises further, changing colour to dull brown.

Tips

- Ensure packing only occurs when the meat is less than 2°C as low temperatures favour deeper oxygen penetration.

Be aware of…

- Meat that is more than 2 days old should not be overwrapped.
- Meat that has been stored for long periods as it discolours more rapidly than fresh meat.

b. Modified Atmosphere Packing

What is it?

- Meat is packed under modified atmospheres (MA) that contain higher levels of oxygen and carbon dioxide.
- Microbial deterioration is retarded.

How does it work?

- The uPVC or expanded polystyrene packs are formed to produce trays from a web of plastic.
- The pack has its air evacuated, flushed with the higher gassed atmosphere and then the meat is sealed therein under a top web of laminated, low permeable barrier film.
- At these higher oxygen concentrations (60-80%), oxygen is able to penetrate almost twice as far into the meat giving a deeper layer of the bright redness.
- The carbon dioxide presence (at 20–40%) prevents pseudomonads from spoiling the meat.

Tips

- Ensure pads are used in each tray as these absorb any released drip.
- 'The colder, the better' (less than 2°C) – once packed, further cooling is difficult.
- Good production standards should provide a colour shelf life of about one week at 1°C.
- Ensure your supplier checks for seal integrity and gas compositions using a gas analyser.

Be aware of…

- Shallow trays – the meat should not come into contact with the lid.
- Meat that has been stored for long periods as it discolours more rapidly than fresh meat.

NOTE: Some chefs believe that meat has been injected or dyed with colour to give a more appetising look for consumers, please see page 35 in Kitchen for more information. This has been countered by modified atmosphere packaging. The colour life of the meat can be extended by placing overwrapped packs in a 'master pack'.

Overwrapping – a process inherited from retail.

Modified atmosphere packaging offers a shelf life of up to one week.

 There are a number of factors pre-slaughter that can limit or increase the shelf life – see Abattoir section for more information.

Overwrapping or Modified Atmosphere Packing – the decision is yours

The summary below should assist in deciding:

OVERWRAPPING	MA PACKAGING
Uses inexpensive equipment and packaging materials	Needs expensive equipment and packaging materials
Requires in-store butchery	Allows centralised packing
Short shelf life (1–2 days)	Longer shelf life (up to 7 days)
Any released drip can leak out	No leakage due to hermetical seal

Source: Meat and Livestock Commission, Shelf Life of Fresh Meat

Note: Meat aged or stored for long periods before packaging significantly affects shelf life.

Mince is a great way to introduce kids to Scotch Beef, Scotch Lamb and Specially Selected Pork.

Mince packaging – a process within a process

The raw material for mince can be frozen meat or fresh meat which is then refined to meet particular specifications. It is derived from the forequarter cuts, hindquarter trim, or both.

What is the process and how does it work?

The manufacture of mince uses a combination of vacuum packing and MA. Prior to mincing, the temperature of the meat needs to be as low as possible (when mince is made from frozen meat, residual ice in the mince keeps temperatures relatively low). Using textbook practice and with MA packaging and transportation in trays allowing free circulation of cold air, mince can be expected to enjoy a shelf life of 7 days.

Tips

• Speak to your supplier if your product appears dull brown.

• Mince is a good base for offsetting the cost of expensive cuts – always try and balance a menu with top price meat items and cost effective ones.

Minced products are also covered by the same Assurance Schemes

For more information on Quality Meat Scotland's Assurance Scheme regarding minced products, contact *info@qmscotland.co.uk*

3. Alternative packaging techniques

Technology is always innovating. Look out for:

• Captech process • Secondary packaging (masterpacks) • Hyperbaric Oxygen

Warning signs

The table below gives a quick reference for packaging problems, their symptoms and manifestations:

EFFECT	POSSIBLE CAUSE
RETAIL PACKS	
Reduction in colour shelf life	• Meat has been aged too long • Temperature abuse during supply chain • Poor quality packaging materials • Faulty seals • Incorrect use of gases (CO_2, O_2, N_2)
Localised browning in MA packs	Meat in contact with the film
Meat appears overly dark	DFD (dark, firm and dry)
Bulging MA packs (using Captech)	Release of carbon dioxide
High drip loss	• Use of frozen meat • Temperature abuse
High microbial numbers, spoilage	• Poor hygienic practice • Temperature abuse • Atypical spoilage bacteria
VACUUM PACKS	
Reduction in colour shelf life	• Using meat aged on bone prior to packing • Temperature abuse • Poor quality packaging materials
'Greening' (putrefaction in 2–3 weeks)	• High pH meat (pH > 6.0) allows hydrogen sulphite producing bacteria to grow • Packaging materials with relatively high oxygen permeability
Gas production through pack expansion	• Spore-forming bacterium, clostridium estertheticum

For more information regarding the influence of packaging on ageing and flavours, see pages 72 – 73.

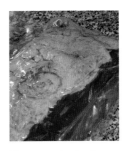

Vacuum packaging is extremely hygienic and 'clean'.

TRACEABILITY – HOW DOES IT WORK?

The Quality Meat Scotland Assurance Scheme guarantees complete traceability throughout the supply chain.

Each animal has a "cattle passport" which tracks all cattle movements as well as movement to the abattoir.

Beef

Ear tags are issued to cattle shortly after birth to help in the identification process and to trace products to farms at the slaughter process. Each animal has a "cattle passport" which tracks all cattle movements (sometimes involving more than one farm) as well as movement to the abattoir.

Only animals which have been born and reared for their whole live on a QMS Assured farm or farms, and slaughtered in a QMS Assured abattoir are eligible to be branded as Scotch Beef. If the animal moves outside Scotland, or to a non-assured farm within Scotland for any length of time, the product is no longer able to use the term 'Scotch'.

 Information on traceability, identification and labelling can be found on pages 16-22.

Lamb

Sheep have a similar system to beef with lambs tagged shortly after birth. On the 1st of January 2010, the European Union changed sheep tagging forever with the compulsory introduction of electronic identification (EID) to further develop the traceability process of lamb from the farm gate. Electronic chips within the new tags help identify animal movements. Details of the animal's history is required when farmers sell either direct to the abattoir or at the market.

As with cattle, only lambs which are born, reared for their whole lives and slaughtered in accordance with the QMS Assurance schemes, are eligible to use the 'Scotch Lamb' brand.

Pork

The identification of pigs from the farm is also vital to identify the origins of the product and help guarantee Quality Assurance at the slaughterhouse. As a legal requirement, all pigs must be clearly identified by a 'slap mark' prior to leaving a unit. This involves using a code (which is unique to each unit) which is then slapped against the pig's shoulder to help identify its origins. The slap mark must be clear enough to allow slaughtermen to identify the pigs origins on the slaughter line in an abattoir. Only pigs which are born, reared for their whole lives and slaughtered in accordance with the QMS Assurance schemes are eligible to use the Specially Selected Pork consumer brand.

WHAT IS MEAT?

The decisions shoppers and diners make about when, what and where to eat drive the industry and never before has there been so much choice. In recent years however, customers are generally more aware of food production with many shoppers more knowledgeable on the practices involved in rearing animals for meat.

Muscle fibre

Meat is muscle tissue which is made up of bundles of long thin fibres. There are two main types of muscle fibres which can be described as being red or white. The proportions of the different fibre types vary between muscles. Red muscles tend to have higher proportions of red fibres. The muscle fibres are bound together in bundles by thin sheets of connective tissue.

Connective tissue is made up from proteins – collagen, elastin and reticulin. Each protein has specific characteristics and reacts differently during cooking. Most importantly, collagen is weakened by heat and forms gelatin, which is soluble. This change helps the meat to become tender.

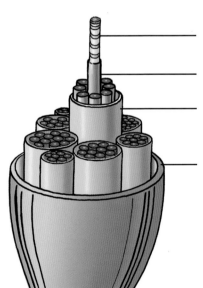

Connective tissue hierarchy

Muscle cell or muscle fibre

Endomysium: connective tissue around a muscle cell

Perimysium: connective tissue around a bundle of muscle fibres

Epimysium: connective tissue around a muscle

i For more information, log onto www.nutrition.org.uk

Why does meat colour vary?

Depending on certain atmospheric conditions, red meat can change colour quite significantly and appear anywhere between bright red and dark brown. This is due to concentrations in the air of various gases and the reaction the meat pigment myoglobin has to it. The following diagrams and images explain this:

Myoglobin and its equilibrium with oxymyoglobin and metmyoglobin

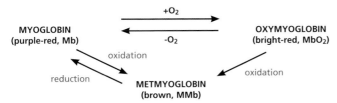

Development of colour at the surface of meat

The colour of meat is determined by the concentration of myoglobin and its chemical state. Myoglobin is the primary meat pigment existing as:

Myoglobin (Mb, purple-red) – myoglobin is favoured by zero oxygen concentration.

Mb predominates as no O_2 is present. This is the case with vacuum packing.

Metmyoglobin (MMb, brown) – metmyoglobin is favoured by low oxygen concentration.

MbO_2 predominates at the meat surface, MMb layer forms at lower levels where O_2 is low, Mb predominates at meat centre where no O_2 is present.

Oxymyoglobin (MbO_2, bright red) – oxymyoglobin is favoured by high oxygen concentration.

With time, MMb layer thickens and extends to the meat surface, 'browning' and discolouring it.

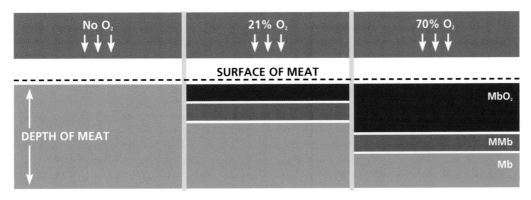

- **myoglobin** (Mb) a principle haem containing pigment in muscle tissue responsible for storing oxygen in muscle and associated with muscle colour.

- **haem** the chemical group that contains iron. A greater haem concentration in the muscle will cause meat to look redder or darker and is likely to be an indication of more red oxidative fibres in the muscle which is characteristic of red meats.

Source: Meat and Livestock Commission

MARBLING

Marbling is a key visual identifier but does it affect meat eating quality?

Fat is critical to the flavour of meat and helps differentiate one meat from another. In fact, research has shown that if all traces of fat are stripped from a piece of lamb and a piece of beef, it is almost impossible to set them apart. Aside from the external layer of fat just beneath the surface of the skin, there is another presence of fat in the animals – what we call 'marbling'. This develops over time so is more predominant in beef or mutton than lamb or pork. In short, marbling is small streaks of intramuscular fat that are found in the muscle. It has a beneficial effect on juiciness and flavour by 'melting' through its surroundings during the cooking process (see graph below).

Aside from the external layer of fat just beneath the surface of the skin, there is another presence of fat in the animals – what we call 'marbling'.

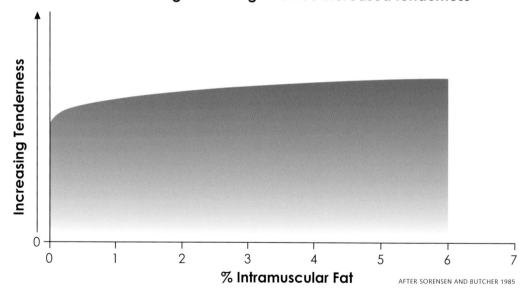

Increased marbling does not guarantee increased tenderness

Increasing Tenderness (y-axis)

% Intramuscular Fat (x-axis): 0 1 2 3 4 5 6 7

AFTER SORENSEN AND BUTCHER 1985

Source: Meat and Livestock Commission 'A Glossary of Carcase and Meat Quality Terms', 1999

For more information about flavour and fat see pages 24–27 in Plate section.

As described in 'Plate', fat is a complex and much misunderstood component in meat. The following definitions should help:

"The adipose (fatty) tissue found in the body. Fat exists both within (intermuscular fat and intramuscular fat) and surrounding (subcutaneous) the lean tissue of the carcase."

"Intermuscular fat is the fatty tissue formed by depots of fat cells situated between the muscles. Along with marbling, intermuscular fat adds to the juiciness and flavour of meat."

"Intramuscular fat is the fat found within the muscles. Visible depots of intramuscular fat are known as marbling."

"Subcutaneous means beneath the layers of skin (or rind) and is most commonly used to describe backfat."

Fat adds specific species flavour and aids the entrapment of moisture within the meat. During the cooking process, fat keeps meat moist and succulent. Grass fed marbling offers a more beef flavour and grain fed a more fatty flavour.

Intermuscular fat – fat between muscle.

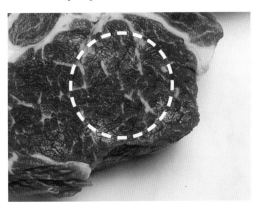
Intramuscular fat, 'marbling' – fat within muscle.

Subcutaneous fat – 'under' skin.

The increase of marbling in a steak or joint will not necessarily mean an increase in tenderness, although there may be some flavour enhancement.

THE IMPORTANCE OF SPECIFICATIONS

For the professional caterer, specifications are vital to ensure a consistency of product supplied to the kitchen. Ultimately, specifications are communication tools – allowing the chef to tightly detail what is required and leaves no uncertainty. It is vital that the supplier delivers to the correct 'spec' every time – not what he / she thinks you want (and certainly not what he / she think they can get away with). The specification example below shows the type and level of information you need to be communicating to your butcher.

Cut: Sirloin Steaks (Country of Origin – Scotch)

Ageing: 14 days on the bone prior to slicing.

Fat Level: Maximum fat depth not to exceed 15mm at any point.

Portion Wt: 225g with a 15g tolerance.

Packaging: Vacuum packed 4 steaks per pack.

Labelling: To include: Name and address of the butcher, origin Scotland, slaughtered in the Scotland (plant number), cutting in Scotland (plant number), traceability code, product name.

1. Boneless 2 rib sirloin

2. Remove the chain

3. Remove visible gristle and connective tissue

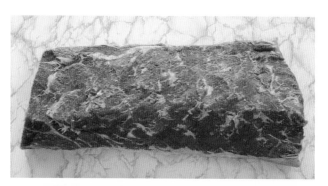

4. Remove back strap (5cm wide) and trim the tail (2cm from the tip of the eye muscle)

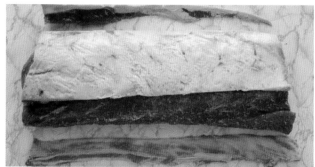

 Very precise specifications will involve additional labour and therefore cost to meet your requirements.

5. Trim fat to a maximum depth of 15mm

6. Remove 3-4 steaks from the rump end until gristle in the centre of the steak has disappeared

7. Remainder of the sirloin to be cut into steaks 2cm thick

8. Steaks to be of even thickness (not wedge shaped)

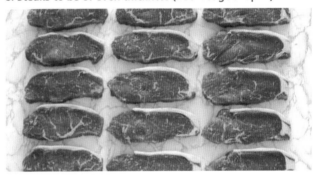

9. To be vacuum packed a maximum of 2 days prior to delivery

Waste Management

This is the waste removed from the 2 rib sirloin. Either you, your butcher or your customer will have to trim off. Make sure you specify what you require.

 Forequarter and fillet cuts do not need the same maturation as hindquarter cuts. Ageing meat carcases lose weight due to evaporation. See page 92.

SUPPLY CHAIN FOCUS
EXPERTLY CUTTING TO ORDER

The catering butcher is a vital link between the abattoir and the kitchen; a good butcher is an invaluable support to the chef.

The best catering butchers are used to exacting and sometimes unique demands from their customers. Their range of services includes, of course, boning and trimming to Meat Buyers Guide specifications as well as a comprehensive range of fresh meat products prepared to larder chef requirements, but they should also be looked upon as a great source of advice and knowledge, a partner in the chef's drive for the best possible quality for his customers.

All meat is of course thoroughly endorsed by farm to table assurance schemes. Scotch Beef, Scotch Lamb and Specially Selected Pork are sourced from farmers with complete traceability, for example Ballindalloch Castle Farm, the original home of the pure Aberdeen Angus herd, and Scotch Lamb from Premier Lamb, raised in the Highlands around Dornoch.

' We only purchase the best. Scotch Beef is renowned throughout the world for its flavour. All discerning chefs expect this."

Alan Healey, Aubrey Allen Ltd,
Proud members of the Scotch Butchers Club.

Meat is hung to individual client specifications – beef can be for a minimum of 21 days but frequently up to 35 days. Lamb is hung for 5 to 10 days depending on the season whilst pork is generally hung for between 3 to a maximum of 12 days.

Meat processing by the larger butchers may be carried out by teams and take place over shifts almost 24/7 to ensure that there is a delivery of fresh meat every day, yet with the best butchers this is never at the expense of quality. On arrival, the meat is weighed and sent to a holding fridge where it will subsequently be retrieved and broken down. The abattoir's tag will allow staff to trace each animal back to the farm, ascertain date of birth, breed and ownership in a matter of minutes should this

Good catering butchers are highly trained and highly skilled: chefs can make good use of their knowledge. A minimum training requirement need

Specifications are the key document for the catering butcher. They are computer generated and kept on file.

Once cut to specification, each pack is verified and labelled accordingly.

The carcase is broken down by a team of expertly trained butchers according to the client's specification.

The specification is the key to good understanding between butcher and customer: many butchers record their clients' specification information – preferred packaging, cuts, quantities – so that the information can be readily retrieved for each new order. This saves time for the clients as well – telesales can understand buying patterns and do not need to re-key information. The client's file is updated as and when menu cycles change and new specifications are required. Once prepared to client specifications, the meat is dispatched, either in refrigerated vehicles to nearby customers, or for customers further afield, sent overnight to arrive first thing the following morning in carefully packed iced boxes.

A good catering butcher demands an excellent quality team and is committed to training its staff. The best butchers are also happy to impart their knowledge to their chef customers, so they can better understand meat eating quality and ultimately buy more wisely for their clientele. Above all, butcher staff should understand and respect the supreme quality of products such as Scotch Beef, Scotch Lamb and Specially Selected Pork.

With thanks to Aubrey Allen Ltd, Coventry.

If you're looking for a reliable butcher, visit www.scotchbutchersclub.org

See page 119.

No. 4
ABATTOIR

The Scottish businesses involved in processing livestock for meat are highly skilled and committed to the highest standards of animal welfare, safety and hygiene.

ANIMAL WELFARE FROM FARM TO ABATTOIR

Only animals born and raised on QMS Assured farms, but also slaughtered in QMS Approved slaughterhouses in Scotland, can achieve the prized consumer branding: Scotch Beef, Scotch Lamb or Specially Selected Pork.

Only abattoir members of the QMS Scheme can supply you with Scotch Beef, Scotch Lamb and Specially Selected Pork. All are independently inspected a minimum of three times a year. Scottish processors work closely together with the farms that supply them to ensure that the highest standards of animal welfare are maintained up to the point of slaughter. After slaughter each carcase is carefully checked at all stages of processing, boning, trimming, packing, chilling and maturation. The training, skill and care of the processors have a profound effect on the ultimate eating quality of the meat they produce.

Key assurance stages

STAGE 1. Approved processors

An Approved Processor is a business or person holding a valid Certificate of Approval for the production and/or processing of products specified on the Certificate. All abattoirs must be sited in Scotland, must fully comply with the requirements of the relevant Council Directive and must achieve upon inspection, on a regular basis, a pass for both slaughter and cutting operations.

Owing to the growing importance of animal welfare, many pig slaughterhouses in the QMS

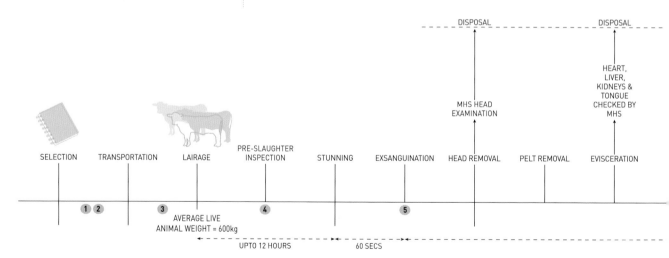

THIS IS FOR CATTLE AND SHEEP, PIGS ARE SIMILAR

 The QMS Processor Assurance Scheme inspects over and above the statutory minimum requirements in particular, by monitoring record keeping and traceability very closely.

Scheme have been approved by the Scottish SPCA, Scotland's animal welfare charity. Although standards of the QMS scheme are already very high, this independent endorsement by the Scottish SPCA can be used by industry as an added marketing tool to help differentiate their products from the competition.

STAGE 2. Animals eligible for slaughter

Scotch Beef is currently derived from prime cattle – cow meat is not permitted to be branded as Scotch. In Scotland, every animal destined to provide Scotch Beef has a passport which records the essential details about the animal. Scotch Lamb is derived from male or female lambs. New season lamb is born, slaughtered and marketed within one year beginning 1st January. All pigs destined to become Specially Selected Pork must be identified with a registered slapmark. For pigs, castration is not permitted in the scheme and all farms must take part in additional health monitoring to ensure high herd health.

In addition, Scotch Beef, Scotch Lamb or Specially Selected Pork must come from farms that are approved members of the Quality Meat Scotland Farm Assurance Scheme.

STAGE 3. Transport from farm to abattoir

Animals must be handled on the farm, in markets and during transport with proper care and concern for their welfare at all times, to comply with the requirements of all appropriate legislation and Codes of Practice. This is important both for animal welfare and because any stresses imposed can trigger the release into the bloodstream of hormones which can affect the final quality of the meat. In Scotland, all animals must be transported to the abattoir by an approved Farm Assured member haulier. The vehicles used have non-slip floors and good ventilation. All loaders, drivers and auction market staff receive appropriate training, and cattle, sheep and pigs are transported in their farm groups wherever possible.

Passport control – the vital documentation for each animal.

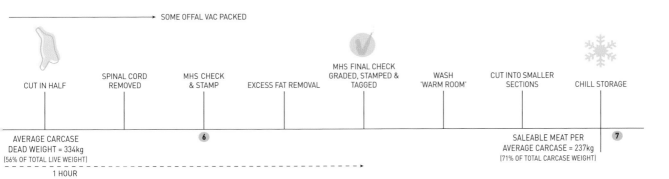

SOME OFFAL VAC PACKED

| CUT IN HALF | SPINAL CORD REMOVED | MHS CHECK & STAMP | EXCESS FAT REMOVAL | MHS FINAL CHECK GRADED, STAMPED & TAGGED | WASH 'WARM ROOM' | CUT INTO SMALLER SECTIONS | CHILL STORAGE |

AVERAGE CARCASE DEAD WEIGHT = 334kg (56% OF TOTAL LIVE WEIGHT)

6

1 HOUR

SALEABLE MEAT PER AVERAGE CARCASE = 237kg (71% OF TOTAL CARCASE WEIGHT)

7

* at R4L classification (71% of side weight); based on Scottish results

 See also the ritual slaughter section in this chapter, page 95.

STAGE 4. On arrival at the abattoir

Animals are unloaded promptly on arrival at the abattoir and stored in an area called the 'lairage'. Lairage and abattoir staff are required to demonstrate competence in relevant welfare standards and adopt practices which ensure humane treatment and minimise stress. The animals are maintained in the groups they were transported in and are given access to fresh drinking water.

Some additional requirements are required of pig processors given their differences to beef and lamb. QMS standards stipulate small gradients (under 30°C) when unloading pigs from their transportation. Within the lairage area, sprinklers must be operated at times and frequencies to enhance the welfare of pigs. Pigs must be slaughtered on the day of arrival but not less than 1 hour after arrival. Suitable bedding must be provided of QMS Assured members.

As part of the traceability process, the ear tag information of cattle, lot numbers of sheep and slap-marks of pigs must be checked before slaughter and all animals undergo a rigorous pre-slaughter inspection by a qualified vet.

STAGE 5. The slaughter process

Slaughter can only be carried out by a trained and licensed slaughter-person. Immediately prior to slaughter, cattle, sheep and pigs are first stunned, rendering them insensible to pain and causing unconsciousness.

In cattle, a captive bolt pistol, which penetrates the skull, is the usual method of stunning the animal. Sheep may be stunned by captive bolt pistol, or by applying an electrical current through the brain. For pigs, animals are rendered unconscious by electrical stunning to the head or compact stunning with CO_2.

See page 95 for details regarding ritual slaughter.

Immediately following stunning, the animal is suspended by its hind legs and cut across the throat, ensuring that at least one of the carotid arteries is severed and so terminating the blood supply to the brain. This is called exsanguination, bleeding or 'sticking'.

The animal is then given 30 seconds to exsanguinate fully at which point the head is 'demasked' by removing all of the head meat so it can be checked by the Meat Hygiene Service in due course.

Front hooves are also quickly removed (the hind hooves subsequently) and 'rodding' is also carried out at this point. With the animal suspended upside down and muscle control now redundant, to avoid the possibility of regurgitation, the oesophagus is skillfully sealed using the 'rodding' technique. There are strict guidelines on the core temperature of the carcase before the carcase moves on to be 'dressed'.

STAGE 6. Dressing the carcase

Soon after slaughter, the animal's body is 'dressed', from which point it is generally referred to as a carcase. The animal's skin is removed (as is the head), and the internal organs are extracted in a process known as evisceration. Evisceration is carried out within minutes of slaughter to reduce the risk of contamination from the organs to the meat.

Carcases are subjected to a rigorous post-slaughter inspection by a qualified Meat Hygiene Service (MHS) inspector. Quality Meat Scotland safety controls are strictly applied and are probably the finest in the world, ensuring every carcase is inspected at several points during the process, not least the internal organs – the liver, kidneys and pluck.

Beef and pork carcases are then split into sides (the vertebrae are split directly through the centre). Carcases are then classified to indicate their commercial value, normally related to the lean meat content and fat cover, retail yield or quality attributes of the meat.

At this point, Scotch Beef and Specially Selected Pork must be clearly identified, and bear as a minimum the slaughterhouse number, date of slaughter, classification and the weight of the carcase. Lamb carcases are left whole but must also be clearly identified as being certified and must bear the slaughterhouse number and slaughter date, classification and the weight.

 Hygiene Assessment Scores (HAS) can be checked online at *www.defra.co.uk*

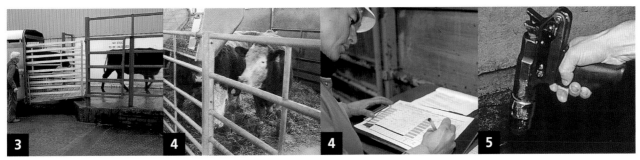

3 All animals are transported to the abattoir by approved QMS members.

4 Animals are maintained in farm groups, kept calm and given access to fresh drinking water.

4 A qualified vet checks arrivals and their documentation pre-slaughter.

5 Stunning renders the animal insensible to pain and causes unconsciousness.

5 The carotid arteries are severed, terminating the blood supply to the brain.

5 The oesophagus is sealed to avoid regurgitation.

6 The animal's hide or pelt is removed.

6 The internal organs are removed within minutes of slaughter to avoid contamination.

6 Organs are checked by a qualified Meat Hygiene Service inspector.

6 Beef and pork carcases are split into sides, lamb carcases are left whole. In both cases the spinal cord is removed.

6 The carcase is stamped to identify it as Specially Selected Pork, Scotch Beef or Scotch Lamb.

6 Each side of beef or whole carcase of lamb is tagged in three places with barcode, weight and grade.

 For further information please visit www.food.gov.uk/scotland

STAGE 7. Chilling and storing

Now the product is transferred promptly to a chilling environment, to restrict the growth of micro-organisms and reduce deterioration. For beef, lamb and pork, the chilling procedure must ensure that in the first 10 hours after slaughter the muscle temperature does not fall below 10°C to avoid over-contraction of the muscles (see cold shortening section on page 97). Thereafter the deep muscle temperature of beef and lamb must be reduced to between 0°C and 7°C as quickly as possible (3°C to 7°C for pork).

STAGE 8. Ageing and hanging

Carcases are held in refrigerated storage for varying periods of time to improve eating quality. Beef and lamb were traditionally suspended on hooks by the Achilles tendon, however more recently, suspending them from the hip via the hole in the bone called the aitch-bone has been recommended as it allows the commercially more important muscles of the carcase to be stretched. Aitch-bone hanging develops these muscles in such a way as to offer better meat eating qualities for the end-customer. Recommended time intervals between slaughter and retail sale for hindquarter beef with aitch-bone suspension are at least 7 days, up to 21 days for better eating quality. For lamb, the recommended interval between slaughter and retail sale is 7 days. For pork, the interval is no less than 2 or 3 days.

STAGE 9. Cutting and packing

Once matured, the meat is supplied for the butcher to break down further, or broken down by the cutting room of the abattoir into primal cuts or joints. The temperature of the meat must not rise above 7°C during meat cutting operations. The meat must be labelled Scotch Beef or Scotch Lamb to indicate that it meets the requirements of these standards.

STAGE 10. Onward distribution to the butcher

Deep muscle temperature must be maintained throughout the period of onward transit from the processor. This is achieved by:

- Transportation in purpose-built, hygienic refrigerated vehicles.

- No contact with vehicle floors during loading, transit or unloading.

- Boxed products not being placed directly on the floor, or carried in the same vehicle as unwrapped carcase meat, unless the boxes are adequately protected.

Specified Risk Material (SRM)

By law, the parts of cattle and sheep most likely to carry BSE must be removed. These parts are known as Specified Risk Material (SRM).

For Beef:

- Kidney, liver, lungs, heart, pancreas, sweetbread, cheeks and tripes are not SRM.

- The tongue must be cut squarely across at the base. Anything forward of the papilli is not SRM. Anything further back towards the tonsils is SRM.

For Lamb:

- Heart, lungs, sweetbread (Thymus), testicles, pancreas, kidney, liver, tongue, casings are not SRM. Illium in any age of sheep is SRM.

Correct at time of printing.

NOTE: In cattle the maximum permitted interval between stunning and sticking is 60 seconds, in sheep it is 15 seconds.

NOTE: Forequarter and fillet cuts do not need the same maturation as hindquarter cuts. For more information on 'ageing' see page 27.

Researchers such as Bishoff (1984) referred to in Jeremiah and Gibson (2003) suggest that beef shrinks by 8-10% during dry ageing irrespective of the environmental conditions and that primal cuts shrink 0.2-0.3% per 24 hours of dry ageing.

Source: Meat and Livestock Commission

See also the section of this chapter called 'Turning muscle into meat', see page 96.

Carcase pH & Temperature

The temperature and pH of the carcase have a major impact on eating quality. The target scores for the carcase post-slaughter are as follows:

TIME	APPROX pH	AV TEMP
At slaughter	7.3	39°C
At 1hr	7.0	39°C
At 3hrs	5.9 – 6.2	38°C
At 10hrs	6.2	34°C
At 1 day	5.5	18°C
At 10 days	5.5	1°C
At 21 days	5.5	1°C

NOTE: Deep leg temperature

Aitch-bone hanging.

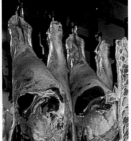

Traditional hanging.

Some abattoirs have in-house butchery whereby the carcase can be broken down into primal cuts before further transportation.

The relationship between carcase pH & temperature

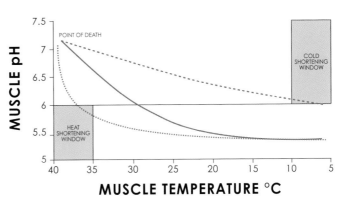

The pH/temperature window used by MSA to optimise the decline in pH relative to the temperature of the muscle. The solid line represents an optimal rate of decline, the dashed line a cold shortening, and the dotted line, a heat shortening scenario.

Source: Meat Standards Australia

Aitch-bone vs traditional Achilles hanging

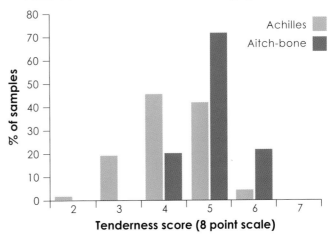

Aitch-bone hanging increases tenderness
Source: DFAS/MLC (1991)

CARCASE YIELD CLASSIFICATION – BEEF, LAMB AND PORK

After all the Meat Hygiene Service checks have been carried out, each carcase is classified. The classification given to the product is vitally important as it dictates the financial revenue for the supply chain.

How Scotch Beef and Scotch Lamb are classified

Beef and Lamb use a scale to reflect the shape (conformation) of the carcase (E, U, R, O, P) and a fat class (1, 2, 3, 4, 5). Taking beef as an example, a product achieving R4L classification has good conformation and a medium fatness – this is the most common classification for a beef steer.

The chart also displays the yield percentage that is to be expected from beef cuts, depending on the classification, for example an R4L will give a 71.1% yield (in other words, 71.1% of this carcase is saleable meat).

Guidelines for conformation and fat class

The following guidelines are considered in understanding the parameters within which 'good' Scotch Beef should sit:

• A minimum of O is widely adopted (to avoid toughness).

• Subcutaneous fat may help to limit cold shortening and so overly lean animals (<3) should be avoided.

• Intramuscular fat may benefit flavour and juiciness but overly fat animals (5H) should be avoided.

For Scotch Lamb, the important factor is driving the balance between 'dry' and 'fatty' meat, neither of which the consumer wants. By finishing Scotch Lambs to a minimum of fat class 2 will give an acceptable 4% or so fat in the meat.

Other beef producers outside the EU use various forms of classification. The main other classification system is from the USDA and specialise for grain-fed animals. Grain-fed means beef especially are fatter, (marbled) than grass-fed and the classification is based mainly on marbling of the muscle.

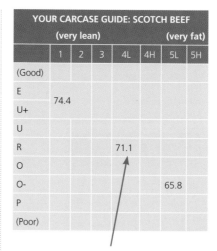

YOUR CARCASE GUIDE: SCOTCH BEEF							
(very lean)					(very fat)		
	1	2	3	4L	4H	5L	5H
(Good)							
E		74.4					
U+							
U							
R				71.1			
O							
O-						65.8	
P							
(Poor)							

R4L is the most common type of steer beef carcase classification

YOUR CARCASE GUIDE: SCOTCH LAMB						
(very lean)					(very fat)	
	1	2	3L	3H	4L	4H	5
(Good)						
E						
U						
R						
O						
P*						

NOTE: A traditionally cut lamb will offer the following saleable meat yields:

• *Fat class 2 – 92.5%*

• *Fat class 4 – 88.8%*

Unlike beef, lamb cuts tend to have a higher proportion of bone-in cuts making it difficult for yield figures to be accurate.

*P values for lamb are sometimes only reported as P with no number, ie. with no fat class sub division.

Classification is a specialised job requiring years of experience

Scotch Beef and Scotch Lamb do not compromise on welfare issues with regard to ritual slaughter methods.

How Specially Selected Pork is classified

Pork products work to a different set of measures, classified in accordance with the EU Pig Carcase Classification Scheme. Only carcases which conform to the following tables are eligible to carry the Specially Selected Pork mark, provided they conform in all other areas of the supply chain.

A probe is used to determine the fat cover of the pork carcase:

YOUR CARCASE GUIDE: SPECIALLY SELECTED PORK		
Weight Range (Kg)	P2 Range (mm)	P1 and P3 Range (mm)
Less than 60.0	7 – 13	14 – 26
60.5 – 70.0	7 – 14	14 – 28
70.5 – 85.0	8 – 15	16 – 30

*Boars 85.0 – 100.0 Kg are only acceptable following a satisfactory on-line taint test.

Ritual slaughter methods in the UK

Some religious faiths have special requirements about the meat that they eat, and in particular the method by which the animal is slaughtered. Scotch Beef and Scotch Lamb do not compromise on welfare issues with regard to these slaughter methods.

Halal slaughter (Muslims)
• The Islamic faith stipulates that only healthy and uninjured animals can be killed for human consumption.
• Although stunning may be considered to be injurious it is carried out in all cases in our schemes, animals must always be stunned for welfare purposes, even if the stunning doesn't kill the animal.
• Death is achieved by drawing a very sharp knife across the throat.

Shechita slaughter (Jews)
• The animals are killed while still conscious.
• The meat is called Kosher (which means 'fit' or 'proper') meat.
• May only be carried out by an approved slaughterman of the Jewish faith who is usually a Rabbi.

 For more information about meeting the needs of Muslim, Jewish, Sikh and Hindu customers, see the Plate chapter of this book, page 12.

TURNING MUSCLE INTO MEAT

Muscle tissue is composed of bundles of elongated cells, called muscle fibres that are densely packed and responsible for the contraction of the muscle in the live animal and for a short time after slaughter. In the living animal, a chemical compound called adenosine triphosphate (ATP) is produced with and without oxygen within muscle cells and acts as a source of energy.

Changes in the muscle after slaughter

a. Rigor mortis

Skeletal muscle remains 'alive' after the slaughter of the animal until the process known as rigor mortis is complete. Following slaughter and exsanguination, the synthesis of ATP in the muscle initially happens and ultimately the ATP, reduced as glycogen (the tissue's energy store), is depleted. Freshly slaughtered 'pre-rigor' meat is tender and pliable, but becomes stiff and tough at the onset of rigor mortis, and then increases in tenderness again as rigor mortis passes and the ageing process begins. The rate at which rigor occurs and is completed is dependent upon a number of factors, such as species, muscle fibre type, temperature and slaughter procedure.

b. Post-mortem acidification

pH is a value used to represent the acidity or alkalinity of muscle and is recorded on a scale of 0 to 14, with values less than 7 referred to as acidic and greater than 7 as alkaline. The pH of muscle in the live animal is approximately 7.3, but this declines rapidly following slaughter to about 5.5 in normal meat, following rigor. This meat acidification is the result of an accumulation of lactic acid. It is generally accepted that a higher 'ultimate pH' (that is, the pH measurement taken after rigor mortis) is associated with increased tenderness and juiciness.

Stress induced 'DFD' meat

Stress induced by poor pre-slaughter handling can cause a limited pH fall, resulting in what is called DFD (dark, firm and dry) meat. DFD is a muscle defect seen in beef and pork carcases but rarely in lamb. It is usually associated with long term stress or prolonged feed withdrawal. An indication of DFD in a carcase is a muscle pH above 6. In addition to its apparent abnormal colour, DFD meat has reduced keeping qualities and is prone to bacterial spoilage.

Even after slaughter, muscle contraction still occurs, visible as 'twitchings'.

 For further information on muscle structure, please see page 78 in the Butcher section.

THE EFFECTS OF TEMPERATURE

Despite the differences between muscles, overall ageing increases meat tenderness. Ageing can also have a marked effect on colour and shelf life. Meat is usually aged by storing it at chill temperatures, either on the bone or in vacuum packed primals, to effect tenderisation. The toughness of meat decreases, quickly at first and then more slowly, due to naturally occurring enzymes in the meat resulting in protein breakdown and a weakening of the muscle structure.

The rate of muscle cooling within the carcase post-mortem is not uniform, even within the same muscle: the centre of a muscle can take a lot longer to cool than the outside edge of a muscle, and the position of a muscle within the body will also determine how quickly and to what degree chilling will take place.

Rapid or blast chilling – as low as -30°C for 30 to 90 minutes – can reduce evaporative weight loss and improve some aspects of carcase quality. However it can also lead to a phenomenon called cold shortening and, unless chilling follows electrical stimulation or pelvic suspension, a reduction in meat tenderness will probably occur.

Shortening and its effect on meat tenderness

Muscle will attempt to shorten if it goes into rigor mortis below about 10°C (called cold shortening) or above 20°C (called hot shortening).

a. Cold shortening
This phenomenon occurs when the muscles are cooled too rapidly after slaughter, while still in a pre-rigor mortis condition. This causes the contractile elements of the muscle fibres to shorten, which results in a very appreciable reduction in the tenderness of meat.

b. Hot shortening
Hot shortening generally produces a lesser shortening and reduction in meat tenderness in comparison to cold shortening.

Electrical stimulation (ES)
The application of an electric current to the carcase following slaughter lowers pH more quickly. The effect is to hasten the onset of rigor mortis in the carcase. Electrical stimulation not only prevents cold shortening but can cause an early tenderisation post mortem, so it can be used to reduce the ageing period – while still producing tender meat.

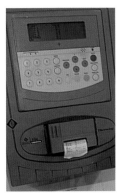

Chill room temperatures are regularly checked.

As well as managing the animal prior to and during slaughter, the plant staff must be diligent with meat post-slaughter.

RESEARCH TOWARDS AN INTEGRATED MEASUREMENT OF MEAT EATING QUALITY (IMEQ)

The production of high quality meat is essential to meet market and consumer requirements, but at present there is no way to measure eating quality at line speed and other methods such as mechanical testing or taste panelling tend to be too slow and/or expensive.

Why work is needed

Previous projects commissioned by Quality Meat Scotland (QMS) and the Scottish Government have identified accurate, reliable and objective techniques for measuring or predicting carcase and meat eating quality in beef cattle and sheep. There is a need to explore the possibility that these techniques can be integrated and combined to work in the abattoir.

What has been achieved so far

QMS and Scottish Government have funded a research and development project aimed at working towards the development of Integrated Measurement of Eating Quality (IMEQ). The project is focused on exploring means to assess meat eating quality in a semi-automatic or automatic manner at line speed in the abattoir. If this research is successful it could provide the potential for the development of value-based marketing systems, genetic improvement programmes and management systems to enhance product quality and process efficiency. The IMEQ project aims to provide the under pinning research which could lead to the development of novel and world-leading technology to assess the eating quality of red meat which could deliver benefits throughout the meat production chain.

The robotic system to measure pH/temperature and carcase fatness.

The project is focused on exploring means to assess meat eating quality in a semi-automatic or automatic manner at line speed in the abattoir.

The measurement technique for carcase fatness, manually tested within the slaughter line.

A new ultrasound probe with custom software provision allows the automatic capture of subcutaneous fat depth at pre-defined anatomical positions on the carcase.

The project is being delivered by a consortium of partners, led by Scottish Agricultural College (SAC). Ongoing abattoir trials are being used to research and develop automated processes to determine the eating quality of meat. These are exploring semi-automatic and automatic means of measuring pH, temperature, carcase fat, carcase grading, meat colour, eating and nutritional qualities. The project aims to examine ways of integrating these measures into a new process for use on the line in abattoirs to replace the current limited system with one which is objective, faster, less labour-intensive and less expensive. The commercialisation of the final IMEQ research output by the industry could then provide producers and processors with a new way to guarantee consumers a consistent eating experience.

The project is developing a unique automatic robotic-based piece of equipment that allows automatic placement of carcase internal pH, temperature and surface-based ultrasound probes at anatomical positions on the carcase. It uses a polar axis robotic manipulator, custom integrated with novel camera technology and custom end-of-arm tooling to support the required sensor test assemblies (pH, temperature and ultrasound probes). This construction has gone through initial testing, and has been integrated with both the pH and ultrasound devices, off-line, in a custom built model installation with full scale model carcase mounted equivalent to that in a commercial carcase line. The assembly is currently undergoing validation testing in the abattoir.

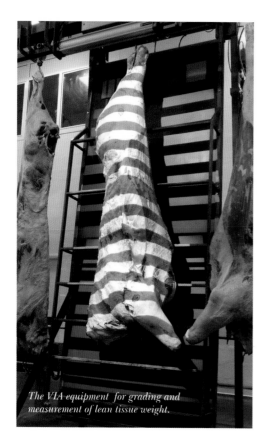

The VIA equipment for grading and measurement of lean tissue weight.

The choice of pH/temperature sensor method has been decided by review, test and suitability for automation and has been trial-attached to an assembly mounted on the end of a robotic arm. The novel camera scans the carcase and generates an automatic 3-dimensional contour map.

An algorithm is being developed to generate landmark positions. These positions will be used to allow the robot to guide the pH/temperature probe to the appropriately pre-defined co-ordinate position adjacent to the target muscle in the half-carcase on-line. The robot manipulator has been

tested off-line and a series of representative trials have been conducted to check its performance. The robot manipulator includes tactile feedback to protect the probe from any possible contact with bone. The robot guides the pH and temperature probe to any required station for interim calibration or cleaning operations.

A new ultrasound probe with custom software provision allows the automatic capture of subcutaneous fat depth at pre-defined anatomical positions on the carcase. The new probe is robust for on-line use, and measures automatically subcutaneous fat depth. Software and hardware development has been carried out and a pilot validation test has been carried. The developed probe will be integrated into the same assembly which holds the pH probe. The robot manipulator arm has been designed to carry out the measurements of the depth of subcutaneous fat using the ultrasound probe.

A number of manual data gathering and performance testing trials have taken place on the abattoir line. This has provided a sufficient dataset to allow the automation software to robustly measure fat depth. Initial results of ultrasonic measurements of fatness compared with those using the "gold standard method" computer tomography indicate that fatness measurements are of substantial accuracy.

A complete commercial VIA system has been installed in the abattoir line, including a bespoke carcase presentation system designed, manufactured and installed in the project. The VIA data gathering computer has been successfully integrated with the IMEQ network and database server on site.

Three principal techniques for prediction of eating and nutritional quality have been investigated

Three principal techniques for prediction of eating and nutritional quality have been investigated in pilot trials.

Above: Vis-NIR equipment to measure meat eating quality and nutritional characteristics.

Left: Vis-NIR probe to measure meat eating quality and nutritional characteristics.

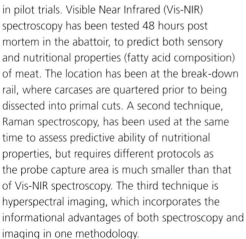

The results showed that there is good discrimination between extreme classes of meat eating quality.

in pilot trials. Visible Near Infrared (Vis-NIR) spectroscopy has been tested 48 hours post mortem in the abattoir, to predict both sensory and nutritional properties (fatty acid composition) of meat. The location has been at the break-down rail, where carcases are quartered prior to being dissected into primal cuts. A second technique, Raman spectroscopy, has been used at the same time to assess predictive ability of nutritional properties, but requires different protocols as the probe capture area is much smaller than that of Vis-NIR spectroscopy. The third technique is hyperspectral imaging, which incorporates the informational advantages of both spectroscopy and imaging in one methodology.

All of these systems have been tested in the pilot trial at the abattoir. Samples will be analysed for both fatty acid composition and sensory qualities.

Based on the analyses, the Vis-NIR spectroscopy is able to offer useful assessments of sensory characteristics. The results showed that there is good discrimination between extreme classes of meat eating quality. This means that almost no observations of the best meat eating quality class have been classified to be in the lowest meat eating quality class compared with a trained taste panel. Considering that this is the pilot trial, results are already very promising.

SUPPLY CHAIN FOCUS
SKILLED, SAFE AND EFFICIENT

Scottish processors participating in the Quality Meat Scotland scheme employ highly trained, highly experienced staff that understand and are proud of their role in producing the highest quality product for their customers.

Efficiency, quality of staff, and constant emphasis on achieving and exceeding standards are the watchwords of the Scotch meat processing industry. Despite the unique nature of their operation, production at the plants is a model of speed and efficiency. Each week the abattoir will decide how many animals it needs and the procurers will go and buy that number, preferably spreading the intake evenly over the week. Some abattoirs also run farms of their own, breeding, feeding and finishing their own cattle, pigs or sheep.

It is vital that the exacting standards and industry demands are consistently met, all Scottish plants work closely with the FSA operations and each is visited by an independent inspector on behalf of Quality Meat Scotland four times a year, including unannounced visits.

The strict requirements begin from arrival into lairage where animal welfare trained staff – both the haulier's and the plant's – unload the animals. Here the animals, in their farm groups for familiarity and to prevent stress levels unduly rising, settle down after the journey. The abattoir's lairage manager ensures all animals are signed in and their passports checked off at reception and then safely segregated off by farm. Most plants receive animals from several different farms in a day and are capable of holding a number of animals in lairage.

Timings are critical: operators have only 60 seconds from the point of stunning to 'stick' each animal. From then on, highly skilled operators set to work in a seamlessly efficient series of stations to prepare the carcase for chilling. Each operator will be proficient in one or more station, requiring differing skills and abilities. The other key timing is that evisceration must have been actioned within 45 minutes of slaughter. After a final passport check each side of beef or lamb carcase is arranged uniformly in the anti cold shortening chiller.

Leaving their mark – traceability continues throughout the abattoir process.

Officials from the FSA operations, the enforcing industry authority, thoroughly check the head, liver, tongue and pluck for contamination and procedures ensure that the head and body relating to these organs can be instantly identified in case of any issues. Likewise the vet is on site until the last animal of the day is killed and all abattoir staff are actively encouraged to closely scan the animal for any signs of cross-contamination. Attention to detail is so thorough that even the temperature of the knife sterilisation baths is checked as part of the quality assurance scheme and a day's clean down takes the best part of six hours.

Evisceration involves the skilled removal of the intestine of the animal. This is done as quickly as possible after slaughter to avoid the risk of cross – contamination.

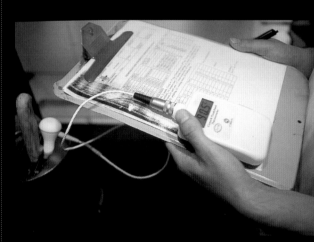

Visual as well as administrative checks are made throughout the slaughter process to ensure traceability and hygiene.

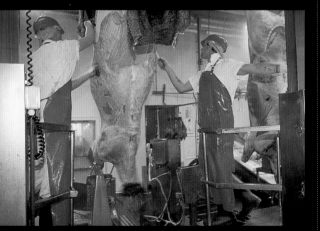

The hide is mechanically removed from the beast and facilitated by two members of the plant's team whose responsibility it is to assist by making small strategic cuts whilst avoiding making any 'tears' to the fat or muscle.

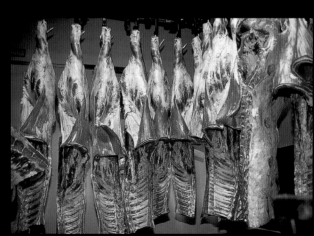

At this plant, initial butchery can be carried out before the meat is onwardly transported. This will be to a specification provided by the customer.

No. 5
FARM

Commitment to excellence begins here, on the farms, hillsides and pastures of Scotland, where cattle, sheep and pig farmers are dedicated equally to the welfare of their animals and to producing meat of the very finest, consistent quality.

AT THE TOP OF THE SUPPLY CHAIN

The farm is the vital first stage in the supply chain, and from the day the animal is born, key decisions are made here that will, during the course of its life, define the eating quality of its meat.

Quality Meat Scotland recommends that where at all possible, a chef should visit a farm to fully understand the importance of the farmer's role in the supply chain.

Quality Meat Scotland and Scotland's farmers are tirelessly committed to close adherence and constant review of the very best farming practices:

- Feeding and management to achieve constant and acceptable growth rates.
- Careful handling and transportation of animals.
- Minimising mixing of unfamiliar animals.
- Ensuring consistent growth.
- Avoiding slaughter soon after diet changes.

Why animal welfare is good for meat quality as well as for the animals

Meat quality and subsequent shelf life can be affected by respect for the animals' welfare, in particular careful handling and transportation immediately prior to slaughter.

Stress triggers the release of hormones such as adrenaline into the bloodstream, stimulating the metabolism of muscles and ultimately meat quality problems in the carcase. There are three main factors that increase the amount of stress:

- Social, for example the mixing of groups of animals, leading to disruption of hierarchy and potential bullying.
- Environmental, such as extremes of temperature.
- Physical, which includes stresses imposed during movement, transportation and slaughter.

The supply chain of Scotch Beef and Scotch Lamb illustrated (from Farmer to Consumer)

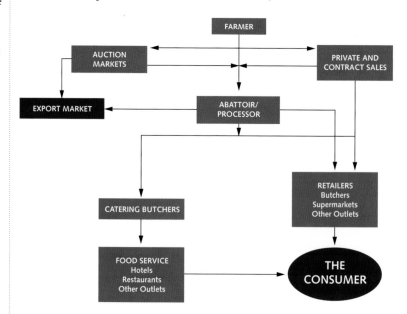

QMS welfare standards were developed with and are endorsed by the Scottish SPCA. Throughout the Scheme, Society Inspectors make regular visits to member farms to ensure compliance with their high animal welfare standards, see page 113.

WHAT INFLUENCE DOES BREED HAVE ON MEAT?

There is considerable debate on the relationship between breed and eating quality. The majority of studies on beef have been carried out on cross-bred animals and tend to show small and/or inconsistent differences. However, significant differences have been found when evaluating beef from pure-bred cattle.

INSIDE KNOWLEDGE

Who's the bos?

Cattle grown in Scotland are from the group called bos taurus, which comprises both beef cattle and dairy breeds which are suited to European climates. Another group, bos indicus or oriental cattle, which have evolved to be able to withstand intemperate climates, are commonly grown in parts of South America and parts of Australia. Bos indicus meat is generally accepted to be less tender than bos taurus, deemed to be the result of the former's slower growth rate.

Source: Factors affecting beef eating quality, Quality Meat Scotland, 2004.

Scotch Beef Aberdeen Angus is renowned for providing meat that satisfies all three consumer demands of tenderness, flavour and juiciness.

In Plate section, fat is looked at in detail in the context of flavour delivery and nutrition, page 13.

What's in a breed?

The majority of Scotch Beef and Scotch Lamb is sourced from a number of breeds which have, over time, proved their ability to thrive in the climate and conditions of Scotland's hillsides and pastures. For cross-breeding, a pure-bred sire is required. Scotland's pig sector tend to use a more limited number of breeds to help improve consistency. A list of the most popular breeds of cattle and sheep are briefly described below.

SHEEP

Scottish Blackface sheep are a traditional Scottish breed and are mainly farmed on the Scottish hills and mountains. Naturally hardy, they live and forage outdoors all year.

Cheviots are white faced sheep from the Scottish Borders, developed to graze hill pastures. Their faces and legs are covered in a fine, hard hair. The fleece is dense and firm. The rams may be horned, but the females are hornless. The Cheviot and its larger relation, the North Country Cheviot, which is farmed mainly in the Highlands, are hardy sheep which live outside all year.

Scotch Mule ewes are crosses sired by Bluefaced Leicester rams out of Scottish Blackface ewes. They are one of the main lamb producing females in Scotland.

Suffolk sheep are the most popular terminal sire breed in the UK. Their progeny, bred from lowland ewes, are early maturing, thanks to their ability to speedily convert milk and grass into meat.

Texel sheep originated from the island of Texel off the north west coast of Holland. Imported into the UK in the early 1970's, they are now the second most popular terminal sire breed. Texels cross well with Scottish breeds to produce lean carcases with excellent conformation.

Scotch Lamb availability. Most Lambs are born from March to May and are ready for processing from June onwards. Spring lambs are born during the spring but are available in summer, autumn and early winter. Easter lambs are born in December. After the 01 January, lambs are commonly called hoggets. Scotch wether lamb is an older lamb and was very popular in Scotland in the past. Wether lamb are older lambs but not as old as mutton. The difference between wether and mutton depends on the finishing, the diet, the environment and the breed.

CATTLE

Aberdeen Angus cattle – one of the favourites with caterers, originated in North East Scotland, but can be found worldwide. In Scotland, Aberdeen Angus bulls are widely crossed with other cattle breeds, producing a nice marbled meat, full of flavour.

Charolais cattle came from France and are popular in the UK thanks to their ability to grow quickly and produce more muscle as a result of larger bundles of muscle fibres.

Limousin, also originally from France, have been popular in the UK since the 1970's. Limousin is now the most popular cattle breed and gives a more delicate meat due to thinner "muscle" fibres and marbling.

Simmental cattle were imported from France, Switzerland and Germany in 1970. Originally bred in Europe for meat, milk and work, UK Simmentals are now bred exclusively for beef production.

Highland cattle are the distinctive hairy, long-horned, native Scottish breed. Their outstanding hardiness enables them to thrive where other breeds would fail. Pure Highland beef satisfies a niche market, thanks to its flavour, marbling and succulence.

Scotch Beef breeds – most cattle born in Scotland are crossbreeds (77%). Cross genetics allow them to adapt to their environment and to optimise economic constraints.

Suffolk sheep are the most popular terminal sire breed in the UK.

Their progeny, bred from lowland ewes, are early maturing, thanks to their ability to speedily convert milk and grass into meat.

Traditional versus continental

Charolais, Limousin and Simmental are called 'continental' breeds for beef, whereas Texel and Charollais are 'continental' breeds for lamb. These breeds have been used in Scotland for decades to improve yield and productivity. Often Scotch Beef or Scotch Lamb would be produced from animals crossed between 'Scottish' breeds and 'continental' breeds. The main Scottish traditional breeds are Aberdeen Angus, Galloways, Luing, Scottish Shorthorns, and Highland for beef and Scottish Blackface, North Country Cheviots, Hebridean and Shetland for lamb.

Variety is the spice of life

Quality Meat Scotland is committed to developing recognition of the qualities and value of Scotch Beef, Scotch Lamb and Specially Selected Pork from both traditional and rare breeds.

Many of the rarer breeds have evolved over time to thrive in different environments and conditions which in turn instil enhanced, varied and often unique eating qualities. Although rare breed population growth is modest across each species, consumer awareness and appreciation continues to increase.

The rare breeds

Here are the rare breeds which are currently on the annually updated Rare Breeds Survival Trust (RBST) watchlist:

BEEF	Belted Galloway, Shetland
LAMB	Hebridean, Shetland, Soay
PIGS	British Lop, Large Black, Middle White, Berkshire, Tamworth

The chef's role in breed heritage

The chef and specialist shops (in conjunction with accredited butchers) are key in driving this message to the general public and to continuing the more obscure breeds. A significant number of top restaurants and chefs are already enjoying and promoting the benefits of meat from rare breeds and Quality Meat Scotland and RBST encourage you to champion the variety and quality such products offer.

NOTE: Breeds offer only a potential for quality, as grape variety does for wine. Scotland is famous for its traditional breeds but more importantly, Scottish farmers are known for their experience as they will know what is the best breed or cross-breed for their pasture and ways of working.

Hebridean is an ancient and native Scottish sheep. A rare breed, this pure bred lamb produces a distinctive and exceptional flavour.

Belted Galloway cattle

Many of the rarer breeds have evolved over time to thrive in different environments and conditions which in turn instil enhanced, varied and often unique eating qualities.

 A list of the accredited butchers and more rare breed information can be viewed by logging onto *www.rbst.org.uk*

Due to the climate, animals may need at some periods of the year some extra feed especially during winter months, pregnancy and suckling.

Cattle and sheep eat a grass based diet, pigs are omnivorous and have a controlled diet that allows for continuity in flavour.

Scotch Beef and Scotch Lamb are mainly grass-fed animals, which means they eat grass either fresh or dried (in the winter). Due to the climate, animals may need at some periods of the year some extra feed especially during winter months, pregnancy and suckling. The origin and nature of the feed is controlled by quality schemes, which govern Scotch Beef and Scotch Lamb production. All members of the Farm Assurance Scheme must source compounds / blended feedstuffs for their livestock from manufacturers / merchants (mills) which are UFAS approved. This ensures traceability of animal feeding-stuffs (raw materials) through regular,

independent inspections of the businesses and their products. Scotch Beef, Scotch Lamb and Specially Selected Pork are artificial growth hormone free.

A key responsibility of the Scotch Beef, Scotch Lamb and Specially Selected Pork farmer is to provide the right diet for the health and well-being of his animals, aligned with a commercial consideration for the final flavour of the meat. Although feed does have an effect on flavour and may affect the oxidative stability of meat (and therefore shelf life), it has little or no effect on tenderness.

Growth hormones are banned with the QMS Assurance Scheme. Use of drugs on farms is regimented, monitored and only used for veterinary reasons.

The role of diet in ultimate flavour

The composition of the diet influences the products of digestion and hence meat odour, flavour and fat characteristics (and thereby eating qualities).

Within reason, there are only a handful of possible options for the farmer but in conjunction with handling, growth and general good husbandry, the meat can vary quite considerably.

For Scotch Beef, Quality Meat Scotland has published the following conclusions:

- Scotch Beef from grass fed animals may develop off flavours more rapidly than Scotch Beef from grain fed animals. Grass and grass silage fed animals generally produces a better quality of meat in terms of colour and lipid oxidation (rancidity) compared with beef from concentrate fed animals.

- Feed can alter fatty acid composition, flavour and oxidative stability of meat. Forage based feeds tend to give higher levels of n-3 polyunsaturated fatty acids and conjugated linoleic acid and lower saturated fatty acid concentration in Scotch Beef.

- Scotch Beef from pasture fed cattle has a lower ratio of n-6/n-3 polyunsaturated fatty acids than Scotch Beef from steers fed on concentrates.

For Scotch Lamb, Quality Meat Scotland has published the following conclusions:

- Grass or forage fed Scotch Lamb has a more intense lamb flavour than grain fed Scotch Lamb.

- Grass feeding increases muscle n-3 polyunsaturated fatty acid concentrations and improves flavour.

- Concentrate feeding can produce 'abnormal flavours' probably due to low n-3 and higher n-6 polyunsaturated fatty acid concentrations.

- Diets containing high levels of cereals can lead to off flavours and soft fat. If cereals are used they should be used whole not rolled or processed.

- Grass fed Scotch Lamb has similar vitamin E levels to those in lamb fed a concentrate diet.

- It has been suggested that 12 hrs feed withdrawal prior to slaughter may benefit eating quality.

- For grass and foraging based diets, it is beneficial to assess vitamin and mineral levels and supplement as necessary.

Scotland's unique mix of environment and natural grazing ensures great-tasting meat.

QUALITY MEAT SCOTLAND FARM ASSURANCE SCHEME

Throughout the Quality Meat Scotland supply chain, comprehensive assurances ensure that the best quality product is available to the consumer, and that begins at the farm.

Our quality assurance scheme is voluntary, it aims to deliver best practices to the industry, based on tradition and science. Consumer demands are also an important part of the scheme review.

Scotland's red meat industry was one of the first to answer the market needs for offering assured products. For Scotch Beef, Scotch Lamb and Specially Selected Pork, Quality Meat Scotland has created specific farm standards of its own which are developed by the industry, for the industry to deliver the best product to the consumer.

The Standards Setting Committees for the QMS Cattle and Sheep Scheme and QMS Pig Scheme consist of farmers, processors, stakeholders, scientists and consumers on whose knowledgeable and experienced shoulders rests the establishment and upholding of required assurance measures. Industry organisations are actively invited to suggest changes and improvements and, if appropriate, they are presented to the Quality Meat Scotland Board. Assurance, however, does not stop at the farm. The entire supply chain is closely assessed and managed.

Where changes to the Standards are made, it is largely as a result of one of three circumstances:

• Industry best practice improvements.

• Changing consumer needs – with food interest and knowledge ever developing, the consumer will continue to be the main driving force.

• Change in legislation – generally consumer driven but constantly under evolution.

Commercially, it is very much in the farm's best interest to apply and achieve assured status. An assessor will inspect all Cattle and Sheep members on an annual basis to ensure best practice continues and a number of spot inspections are also carried out each year. Pigs assessment frequencies depend on the existing standards on the unit and, at the very minimum take place every 18 months. All farms in the QMS Pig Scheme must have advisory veterinary visits every three months and must participate in national herd health developments such as the Zoonosis Action Plan.

All standards are available online by visiting **www.qmscotland.co.uk** and clicking on the 'Assurance Programmes' tab.

Scotland's comprehensive assurances of quality and provenance begin at the farm.

 For more information about the complexity and diversity of controls at each stage of the supply chain, visit *www.qmscotland.co.uk*

ANIMAL WELFARE

Animal welfare is a priority for those in the Quality Meat Scotland assurance chain. QMS welfare standards are developed with, and are endorsed by the Scottish SPCA*, Scotland's animal welfare charity. For the QMS Cattle and Sheep Scheme, Scottish SPCA inspectors make regular visits to a percentage of member farms to ensure compliance with the high animal welfare standards.

For the QMS Pig Scheme, all units are inspected to highlight the already high welfare standards on-farm. A recent project, launched in 2009, has developed this collaboration with key marketing activities now communicating the association alongside the industry's customers. The initiative with Scotland's pig sector and four other partners was awarded for collaborative working at the 2010 Scotland Food & Drink awards.

*Established in 1839 to prevent cruelty to animals and promote kindness and humanity in their treatment, the Scottish Society for the Prevention of Cruelty to Animals is Scotland's leading animal welfare charity. For further information, contact the Scottish SPCA on 03000 999 999 or visit www.scottishspca.org

SCOTTISH **SPCA**
Scotland's Animal Welfare Charity

It is in Scottish livestock farmers' best interests to achieve Quality Meat Scotland Assured status.

How assurance standards are set for all stages of Scotch Beef and Scotch Lamb production

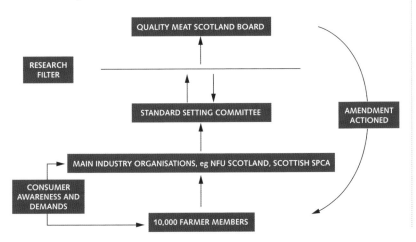

 On-farm assurance is independently audited to EN45011 standards.

Scotch assurance: comprehensive and progressive

Through all stages of the animal's lifetime, significant processes and practices are adhered to and monitored to ensure the best quality of life and superior final product to your consumers. This chart shows how rigorous and fundamental the Scottish scheme is.

Stress-free transportation and handling shows respect for the animal and delivers finer meat.

Animal welfare from birth to slaughter, is a priority to all involved in the industry.

Portfolio of disciplines that are required to attain farm assurance

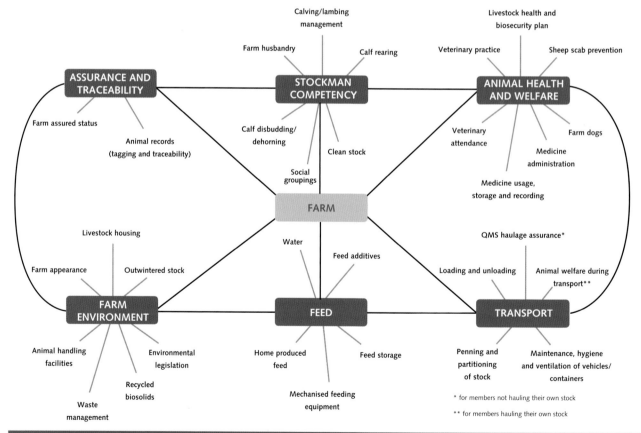

 For further information on muscle structure, please see Butcher, page 78.

NOT ALL SCOTTISH BEEF AND LAMB ARE SCOTCH

The decisions shoppers and diners make about when, what and where to eat drive the industry and never before has there been so much choice. In recent years however, customers are generally more aware of food production with many shoppers more knowledgeable on the practices involved in rearing animals for meat.

Scotch

'Scotch Beef' and 'Scotch Lamb' must be born, reared all their life in Scotland and slaughtered in Scotland, and must be Quality Assured. 'Scotch Beef' and 'Scotch Lamb' labels have Protected Geographical Indication (PGI) status under European Council Regulation 2081/92.

Scottish

Use of the 'Scottish Beef' (or Product of Scotland) label does, however, require approval under the Beef Labelling Scheme. To be labelled as 'Scottish' or 'Product of Scotland', cattle must have been born, reared and slaughtered in Scotland but they are not Quality Assured. 'Scotch Beef' is only Quality Assured by Quality Meat Scotland (QMS).

Specially Selected Pork

National Symbols

Scottish national symbols are not a guarantee of origin or quality – saltires, thistles, tartan doesn't make beef or lamb 'Scotch'.

For more information visit:

www.scotland.gov.uk/Topics/Agriculture/Agricultural-Policy/LivestockAndLivestockProd/beef/Labelling

or call QMS on +44 (0)131 472 4040.

Traditional

The term 'Scotch' applies to higher quality food produced in Scotland such as whisky, salmon and of course beef and lamb.

Scotch Beef and Scotch Lamb are guarantees of:

• genuine origin.

• quality scheme.

• better consistency.

SUPPLY CHAIN FOCUS
ONLY THE BEST OF NATURE'S PLAYGROUND

It is in the beautiful countryside and often remote farms of Scotland that the story of Scotch Beef, Scotch Lamb and Specially Selected Pork begins: a story that starts with a passion and respect to produce the best in the world.

Scotland's farmers are justifiably proud to be at the top of the supply chain that produces some of the world's greatest products. Their passion, both as producers and consumers, is unsurpassed. The farmers are part of a supply partnership in which every link depends on the other to maintain quality. With this in mind, they have excellent relationships with the abattoirs they supply and all are part of Quality Meat Scotland's Farm Assured Scheme. Every year, inspectors, independent from Quality Meat Scotland, visit each farm, carefully checking and supporting procedures in terms of husbandry and paperwork.

"You don't get bored of eating good Scotch Beef, we have it two or three times a week and we feel especially good if it's ours from the local butcher."

Willie Ritch

The cattle passport system is viewed by Scottish farmers as a major innovation, which adds provenance and reassurance to their product reinforcing their product integrity further. For generations, Scottish stockmen have used their knowledge and experience to breed, cross-breed and raise the finest beef cattle, lambs and pigs in the world, and today's farmers use their expertise to ensure that their stock's breeding and

A key moment for all farmers in the life of their stock is the move to the abattoir and so the way animals are selected, transported and handled on arrival at the abattoir by the staff is fundamental to delivering only the finest end product. But of course none of this happens until the animals' traceability mechanisms are checked – allowing a longevity of traceability throughout the products' supply chain.

With thanks to Willie Ritch of East Fingask Farm, Aberdeenshire.

The key to the unique quality of Scotch red meat is the farm's pasture land, the farmer's care and attention and the animals' overall welfare.

THE SCOTCH BEEF CLUB

The decisions shoppers and diners make about when, what and where to eat drive the industry and never before has there been so much choice. In recent years however, customers are generally more aware of food production with many shoppers more knowledgeable on the practices involved in rearing animals for meat.

The Scotch Beef Club looks for member restaurants who embrace best practice and high levels of service and who wish to promote Scotch Beef, Scotch Lamb or Specially Selected Pork because they know and believe in their outstanding quality. Membership is not restricted to Michelin starred establishments or high profile venues – although we are proud to say that many members do fall into this category. The Scotch Beef Club encourages best practice and members are ambassadors for fresh, well-produced food which meets the highest farming and traceability standards. Like the farmers, Scotch Beef Club members care about welfare, the environment and most importantly, their customers.

Membership of the Scotch Beef Club will benefit both you and your customers. Firstly, it will give you the confidence that the meat you serve in your restaurant is exactly what it claims to be. Secondly, it will give your diners the reassurance that you can vouch for the welfare, production and source of the meat that you serve.

The Scotch Beef Academy runs in conjunction with the Scotch Beef Club and members will have the opportunity to participate in practical courses to increase their working knowledge of Scotch Beef, Scotch Lamb and Specially Selected Pork and how to make the most of them in your particular restaurant.

Quality Meat Scotland aims to ensure that members of the Scotch Beef Club will be better informed about the meat they serve, will ask more of their suppliers and will, in turn, offer more information to their customers.

How to apply for membership?

Firstly, can you answer 'yes' to the following 5 questions?

1. **Is the origin of meat important to you and your clientele?**
2. **Do you currently purchase Scotch Beef?**
3. **Do you identify Scotch Beef on your menu?**
4. **Do you offer at least one Scotch Beef dish on the majority of your menus?**
5. **Do you want to know more about meat?**

If you have answered yes then you need to email the following details to: *info@qmscotland.co.uk*

Name • Establishment Name • Address • Town • Postcode • Tel No • Email address • Current Scotch Beef dish on menu

Membership application packs will be sent to you directly from Quality Meat Scotland, please contact QMS directly for further information and membership details. Applications will be considered on merit and up to 20% of establishments will be subjected to a random traceability audit each year.

THE SCOTCH BEEF CLUB

 www.scotchbeefclub.org

SCOTCH BUTCHERS CLUB

The Scotch Butchers Club is run by Quality Meat Scotland and is aimed at increasing the stockist availability for Scotch Beef, Scotch Lamb and Specially Selected Pork to chefs and consumers.

Membership is open to any independent retailer sourcing beef, lamb and pork from an approved supplier and who can confidently label their products "Scotch" or "Specially Selected Pork". A small membership fee offers the opportunity to drive business and look forward to increased sales through this marketing advantage.

Membership is divided in 2 categories: Butchers and Catering Butchers. Butchers are independent retailers whose main activity is retailing to consumers. Catering Butchers are retailers whose main business is to supply to foodservice. Please note that some catering butchers may also have high street outlets. Equally, some butchers would supply local foodservice. Membership is open to independent retailers sourcing beef, lamb and pork from approved suppliers – QMS monitors suppliers to make sure you get the genuine products, Scotch Beef, Scotch Lamb and Specially Selected Pork.

Butchers have to pay a small membership fee to help produce information and promotional material about the products and the schemes.

If you are looking to find your local butcher or caterer supplying genuine Scotch Beef, Scotch Lamb or Specially Selected Pork, check our website www.scotchbutchersclub.org

For more information regarding the Club activities contact
info@qmscotland.co.uk

UK locations of Scotch Butchers Club members

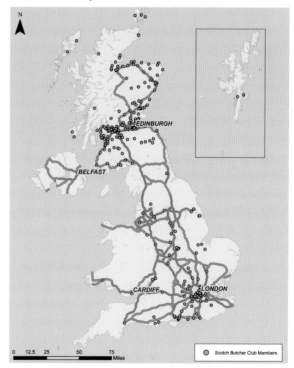

Correct at time of printing

 www.scotchbutchersclub.org